WHY YOGA IS
YOUR KEY TO
HEALTH, HARMONY AND VITALITY

One of the purposes of ancient yoga was to delay the bodily effects of age so that the yogi could have more time to perfect his techniques. The benefits of these practices are now widely recognized in the West for their great beneficial effects on almost all areas of the body—circulation, digestion, nerves, joints, muscles, organs and glands. Certain positions have been found to have stimulatory results on both male and female reproduction systems.

And yoga's emphasis on correct breathing and knowledge of relaxation helps to bring inner peace and to preserve and recharge vital energy—all easy to learn and indispensable in maintaining sexual youth and vigor.

By the famous authors of **Yoga For Women**
and **Yoga Over Forty**

D1604372

Sex and Yoga

By Nancy Phelan and Michael Volin

BANTAM BOOKS · TORONTO · NEW YORK · LONDON

SEX AND YOGA

*A Bantam Book / published by arrangement with
Harper & Row, Publishers, Incorporated*

PRINTING HISTORY
*Harper & Row edition published January 1968
Bantam edition published July 1969*

*Bantam Books are published by Bantam Books, Inc., a subsidiary
of Grosset & Dunlap, Inc. Its trade-mark, consisting of the words
"Bantam Books" and the portrayal of a bantam, is registered in the
United States Patent Office and in other countries. Marca Registrada.
Bantam Books, Inc., 271 Madison Avenue, New York, N.Y. 10016.*

Contents

Sex and Yoga

Authors' Note

Hatha yoga has become so much part of western life that inevitably it must be considered in relation to sex.

The question most frequently asked is whether its practice could be reconciled with normal family life. The answer, that yogis have been householders and fathers of children, often causes surprise, for in the West *yogi* is usually identified with *ascetic*.

This book attempts to give a general outline of the ways in which sex and yoga are inter-related. This has necessitated the inclusion of a certain amount of background information on yoga's purpose and philosophy, for without some understanding of the spiritual teachings many practices would appear meaningless—even absurd. Though some techniques may seem strange to the West, they are part of spiritual training.

Since the word *yoga* means essentially a method of reuniting the individual spirit with the Universal Spirit, it could in fact be used for any practice inspired by this aim. There are, in the East, so many yogas and off-shoots of yoga that to avoid confusion we have used the term 'classical' for such familiar forms as *Hatha, Rajah, Karma, Jnani* etc; generally speaking, those yogas that have either been laid down in sacred writings or in the texts.

In the *Bhagavata Purana,* the god Krishna says, 'My worship is of 3 kinds, Vedic, Tantric and mixed. A man should worship me in whichever of these 3 ways he prefers.' If *Vedic* is interpreted as the path of austerity and celibacy, *Tantric* as the path of experience, and *mixed,* as the path of the householder, this book will be found, roughly, to follow these headings.

Yoga and Sex

Use of sexual energy in yoga training. The purpose and aim of yoga. Karma and Rebirth. The path of Celibacy; the Tantric path; the path of the Householder. Yogas suitable for Householders. Yoga and sex in everyday life.

Although the words *sex* and *yoga* are often held to be incompatible, in certain contexts they are closely related. In yoga, sexual energy is recognized as a powerful force which, when harnessed by knowledge and control becomes an additional means of attaining the ultimate goal.

Yoga means union. The word comes from the Sanscrit root *yuj*—to yoke or join, and is used to describe an ancient method of physical, mental and spiritual training, accepted as one of India's six great philosophical systems. Unlike some eastern schools of thought, yoga recognizes the existence of God (*Isvara*). It is, as it were, inter-religious, in that its practice does not conflict with individual beliefs; on the contrary, it contributes to and intensifies spiritual awareness. Its teaching that the things of this world are transient, its disciplines for developing moral strength, and its fundamental aim—to find God—are common to all great theistic faiths of East and West. According to personal preference it could be regarded as a private religion, a way of life, a form of character training or simply a means of improving health and bodily strength.

In the transition from east to west the teachings inevitably suffered a certain amount of change. Full observance of ascetic disciplines, for instance, would be extremely difficult, if not impossible, for westerners living in

urban conditions; yet adaptation does not necessarily
mean complete loss of the message. Though we cannot all
live in seclusion or abandon responsibilities and material
commitments we could all, in our personal lives, try to
follow this noble philosophy.

To most of us the name yoga is identified with special-
ized training, austerities, specific practices, with certain
schools of thought, each with their own individual methods and techniques; yet in its fullest sense it is not limited
to these 'classical' forms. Good deeds, generosity, compassion, unselfishness, kindliness, nobility are all methods
of yoga, all means of transcending the ego, a necessary
step on the path to union with the Divine Principle—the
final aim of all methods and paths.

To most of us 'Self' and ego are identical . . . the 'I'
that experiences desire, ambition, misery, happiness; that
performs actions, and fears extinction with death; but in
yoga it is taught that the true Self is pure Spirit, (*Atman*)
a living spirit inhabiting a bodily temple, unchangeable,
indestructible, untouchable by pain, grief, misery, by 'the
world's slow stain . . .' a part of the Universal Spirit
(*Brahman*).

In our ignorance we believe that we (or the Self) are
part of the world we live in; but the world is Matter, not
Spirit. Spirit and Matter cannot be reconciled, therefore
the Self can never be identified with the dimensional
world. Until this is accepted we are at its mercy. Until we
understand that the essential Self cannot be affected or
destroyed by life's trials and hardships we must suffer.

If detachment from the material world brings freedom,
even greater freedom comes from ability to distinguish
the true Self from the ego, the physical-mental personality. He who has achieved Self-realization has a true perspective on life. He knows, like St Augustine, that 'When
once more I shall be united to Thee with all my being,
there shall be no more grief and toil, and my life will be
alive, filled wholly with Thee.'

Purely intellectual understanding of Realization is not
enough, for the mind, being Matter, can give no more
than a reflected view of the Spirit Self, as a crystal reflects

colour from an object without becoming that object.*
Full comprehension, face-to-face experience by union of
individual spirit with Universal Spirit can only come
through revelation, in a state of super-consciousness
known as *samadhi*, in which the mind plays no part and
in which all thought is suspended. Different yogas employ
different methods for reaching *samadhi*. In some of the
Tantric schools and cults this state of suspension is known
by other names, but the intention is always liberation of
the spirit.

Even to experience it briefly is to possess the key of the
prison. Nothing else has equal importance to the 'liberated' man. He is complete; he has found his way home;
he has become reunited with that part of his being lost at
birth, when his spirit took on flesh and entered this world.

This nostalgia, this homesickness, this longing to find
the way back is the inspiration behind yoga.

KARMA AND REBIRTH (Reincarnation)

There can be no real appreciation of yoga or its methods
without understanding the significance of karma.

Karma and Rebirth (reincarnation, metempsychosis,
transmigration of souls) are twin doctrines. They cannot
be separated, for without belief in reincarnation there is
no belief in karma or necessity for karmic laws. Bound
together, they must be discussed together.

Belief in karma is not peculiar to yoga; it is fundamental in all Oriental philosophies and many religions . . .
Buddhist, Hindu, Taoist. Rebirth was one of the main
doctrines of Christianity until abandoned by the Council
of Churches at Constantinople in the 6th Century.

The word *Karma* is derived from the Sanscrit root *kri*
—to do or make, which explains the soul of the doctrine.
Action creates karma; deeds, good or bad, evoke karmic
laws.

Materially, it is a law of cause and effect, action and

---

* Patanjali: *Yoga Sutras*. Though often referred to as the Father of
Yoga, Patanjali was not its creator. The system was already centuries
old when he collected and clarified the *sutras* (aphorisms) . . . some
scholars believe in the 3rd century, others say much earlier.

reaction; spiritually, a law of moral retribution. He who
sets the cause in motion suffers the effect. We reap as we
sow.

Probably more than half the thinking world, as well as
very primitive races, accept some form of reincarnation.
Many African tribes, Pacific Islanders, Australian aborig-
ines believe in ghosts that come back to tribal grounds or
villages after physical death. From time immemorial,
through the teachings of ancient Egyptians, Chinese,
Chaldeans, Druids, to modern religious thought, a strong
conviction persists that a part of human make-up is indestructible. Whether known as soul, true self, divine
spark, vital energy, the meaning is the same.

To accept immortality of the soul is to raise the question of life after physical death. The doctrine of rebirth
teaches that the soul is reincarnated through another
body, after a period of time governed by karmic laws.
Chinese and Indian peasants often put their dead children
by the roadside in an attempt to shorten this time, hoping
that since many pregnant women will pass, the dead
child's soul could enter the body of an unborn one.

Between 'death' and 'life', souls travel or transmigrate
from body to body, often bringing with them, in varying
degrees, impressions of previous lives. 'Not in entire for-
getfulness and not in utter nakedness, but trailing clouds
of glory do we come . . .' 'Oh joy, that in our embers, is
something that remembers.' Many poets have known this
instinctively whether or not they formally accepted the
doctrine; its possibilities have always fascinated writers
and thinkers, and there can be few of us who have not at
some time known the feeling . . . *This has happened before. I have been here before.*

Genius in children . . . Mozart . . . Rembrandt . . .
Euclid . . . has often been attributed to reincarnation.
Heredity is no convincing explanation, for very simple, il-
literate peasants have given birth to genius.

Though karmic law is universal, man creates his own
karma. The *Dhammapada* says: 'All that we are is the result of what we thought; it is founded on our thoughts; it
is made up of our thoughts.'

'If a man speaks or acts with an evil thought, pain follows him as the wheel follows the foot of him who draws

the carriage. But if a man speaks or acts with a pure thought, happiness follows him like a shadow that never leaves him.'

It is taught that there are three kinds of karma for every life: (i) accumulated *past* karma, not worked out; (ii) the karma allocated at birth, (destiny), influencing *present* life; and (iii) the karma created during the present incarnation, influencing *future* lives.

The highest state of all is complete freedom from karma and the wheel of death and rebirth. In the whole history of man, only a few have achieved this supreme perfection. Among such enlightened souls, yoga includes Jesus Christ, Mohammed, Buddha and Krishna.

'Karma is an undeviating and unerring tendency in the universe to restore equilibrium and it operates incessantly,' said W. Q. Judge in his *Karmic Aphorisms;* yet though undeviating there is nothing sinister in this law. We are not its slaves. Karma from previous incarnations may lead us into circumstances in which it is difficult to avoid or refrain from action, but it cannot *compel* us to any act in the present life. Most of us, in our limited state of development might succumb, but we all have the choice of exerting free will, of rising above circumstances.

By this free will we could overcome, in varying degrees, karmic influence and gain victory, not only in this life, but in future incarnations.

It is believed that apart from personal karma, each race, nation, even all humanity has its karma, governed in very much the same way as for individuals.

Experiments in 'mind-opening' drugs suggest we may be on the threshold of scientific proof of reincarnation and immortality of the soul. Under these drugs, subjects have spoken languages never heard before, described countries never seen, revealed knowledge never consciously acquired. It is possible that we all know far more than could be gained in one life; that perhaps *everything* is stored on 'dark shelves' of the mind, awaiting the key that will unlock the door.

METHODS OF YOGA

There are a number of recognized paths towards liberation: *Karma yoga,* the path of right action; *Rajah yoga*
—of complete control of the mind; *Jnana yoga,*—of
knowledge; *Hatha yoga*—of bodily strength and control;
Bhakti yoga—of devotion . . . and others leading into
esoteric fields through sound, vibration, geometrical
forms, rousing of latent powers and higher faculties. All
have the same aim: liberation, reintegration, identification. One travels by the way for which one is best suited
by temperament and inclination. It could be a synthesis
of several paths, for one yoga often merges into another.
All are based on intimate understanding of human physiological functions, mental processes and spiritual needs.
The early sages' knowledge of the subconscious mind, its
importance and power is considered by some contempo-
rary writers far more profound than that of modern psy-
chologists.

For the West, *Karma yoga,* the path of right action,
and *Hatha yoga,* of bodily strength and control, are the
most practical.

The *Karma yogi* is usually a householder, working,
raising a family, fulfilling his obligations to society, leading a normal domestic life. He tries to live by right
thought and action, honourable in his dealings, whole-
hearted in all he does, always with the inner knowledge
of true values . . . of the ephemeral nature of material
possessions, of the eternal nature of the spirit.

Many ordinary people are unconsciously practising
Karma yoga in the conduct of their daily lives. In our
own times, outstanding examples are Group-Captain
Cheshire and his wife, dedicated to compassion, unselfishness and right action.

In *Hatha yoga,* by far the best-known path in the west,
liberation is finally attained through physical and mental
discipline and control of the breath. This leads to mastery
of concentration, contemplation and finally Identification.

Few westerners pursue this path to its conclusion. Most
are satisfied to follow the physical training and enjoy the

benefits that result. This has led to the impression that hatha yoga is nothing but exercises and as such it is sometimes dismissed. The enlightened student, however, knows that it is a form of complete mental and physical discipline which fits him for the rigorous demands of higher stages of training and which could ultimately lead to Self-realization.

The subject of this book—sex in relation to yoga—is discussed under three headings: the path of the Celibate (or Asceticism), the Tantric Path, and the Path of the Householder.

THE ASCETIC YOGI

This is the path of austerity. The rigid disciplines of the ascetics take a man away from family, material responsibility and worldly possessions. Nothing must interfere or stand in the way of his quest for freedom, his training in *stilling* body and mind. Gradually he is led from ordinary consciousness into progressively higher states, always working away from the fluctuating distractions of human life and mental activity towards the suspension in which *samadhi* becomes possible.

The ascetic must have complete control of the senses and observe complete celibacy. Sexual energy must be conserved for increased psychic power; material possessions are renounced for the bondage they bring; absolute detachment from the world is essential.

THE TANTRIC YOGI

Tantrism shares certain features and practices with hatha yoga. In both, stress is laid on the importance of bodily health and perfection; on the idea of the body as an *instrument* by which liberation is achieved; on the desire to achieve complete mastery over the physical shell, thus transmuting it into a divine vehicle. In some Tantric schools the disciple is not an ascetic and celibacy is not practised. Liberation is attained through knowledge, bodily control, experience, through sexual intercourse raised to the level of a religious rite and controlled by yogic methods to bring about physical and mental suspension, leading to liberation.

THE HOUSEHOLDER

The ascetic's complete rejection of everyday life is impractical for all but the few. Though in India it is not unusual for a middle-aged man, having provided for his dependents' future, to leave home and family and seek a *guru* to guide him on the path to liberation, it is rarely possible in the West.

Nor is everyone suited for the monastic life; yet this does not mean disqualification from yoga. As we have seen, there are different paths for different temperaments and mentalities. Many yogis have been householders; it is customary for members of certain sects to marry. The yogi's main objective, when all is said and done, is reunion with the Universal Self. Which path he takes is his own choice, since all lead to the same destination if sincerely followed. He may live in seclusion or out in the world, in celibacy or family life, in a monastery or a palace, as a *swami* * or a business man. The householder, with wife and children, enjoying life but in no way deluded by the world's false values, could in his own way be as good a yogi as the ascetic.

In the East, a teacher who has accepted a young disciple sometimes sends him back to the world, advising him to become a householder, marry, experience the joy of fatherhood; then return to monastic life, purified and enriched by experience.

'The fruit of childhood is liberty, the fruit of youth is in magnificent lusts, the fruit of age is in peace of soul; the fruit of life is to have laboured.'

---

* In the West, the words *swami* and *yogi* are often confused. A *swami* —one seeking union with the Self (*swa*) is a monk, a member of an order, and leads a life of complete renunciation, of celibacy, non-possession and submission to spiritual discipline. Though a man may be both, a *yogi* is not necessarily a *swami*. The meaning of *guru* (spiritual guide) is also frequently confused with *swami*. *Swami*, which also means Master, may be given as an honorary title.

YOGA AND NORMAL SEX-LIFE

The sex drive is nature's method of ensuring continuance of the species. A form of physical immortality is common to all creatures. In the most primitive, the unicellular, the parent cell survives in the new cell which it produces and into which it becomes absorbed, thus cheating physical death; among higher animals which multiply by complete separation the parent lives on, metaphorically, through his descendants, though he himself dies.

The subject of man's need for sexual intercourse has always fascinated thinkers. Explanations for this need range from the most mundane and prosaic to the noblest and most poetic. At one extreme is the suggestion that it is purely a means to discharge physical tension caused by accumulated semen in the seminal vesicles—as the bladder might be emptied; at the other is Plato's theory that man and woman were originally one, divided by angry gods, and are continually striving to reunite. Even loftier is the Tantric belief that union of male and female represents reintegration of soul and Divine Principle . . . a return to primal nonduality.*

We have touched on ways in which celibate and Tantric yogas use sexual energy or sexual intercourse to attain liberation, but such practices have little more than academic interest for the man on the Householder's path. He is more concerned with methods applicable to his own sex life, in increasing and maintaining health and virility for as long as possible.

To many, *sex life* means exclusively the practice of intercourse; yet the meaning is far wider. The years of development, through puberty to maturity, the reproductive system and its disorders, menstruation in women, preg-

---

* 'The Tantrics—like the Ancient Egyptians—exalt right knowledge of the reproductive processes, as no doubt it should be exalted, to the level of a religious science . . . the union of the male and female principles of nature, in what is called in Tibetan, the *yab-yum* (father-mother) attitude, symbolizes completeness, or at-one-ment. Power, symbolized by the male . . . and Wisdom, symbolized by the female . . . are said, esoterically, to be ever in union.'
(Evans-Wenz, W. Y.: Tibetan *Book of the Dead*)

nancy, childbirth, menopause, emotional disturbances, all come under this heading. There are few who require no help in this part of their lives, even if only the simple support of good health.

Though interest in sex is no longer regarded as disgusting, indecent and unhealthy, we are now inclined to go to the other extreme. The subject has not only emerged into the light of day; it has become a public obsession. What was once hidden is now thrust at us from every magazine, cinema and newspaper, treated as a nine-day's wonder.

One basic cause of this excessive attention is that many people lead frustrated or non-existent sex-lives. Doctors, psychiatrists, mental hospitals, social workers all know the extent of unhappiness caused by maladjustment, repression, frustration, loss of potency, frigidity, sterility or just plain loneliness, resulting from lack of someone to love or be loved by. It would be bad enough if these miseries were confined to those who endure them, but almost invariably they react on others, in forms ranging from simple bad-temper to hideous sex crimes.

Sometimes social, religious or economic reasons prevent the enjoyment of a normal sex-life, in which case sublimation is the only healthy alternative. (To sublimate is to direct the sex energy into different channels, unlike repression, which attempts to subjugate it, usually with unhappy results.) Sublimation is not easy for all temperaments; there are many who spend years struggling to control a sexual drive denied natural expression. In such cases, certain sublimative techniques used by celibate yogis could offer some help.

Many problems of sexual maladjustment, inadequacy, lack of confidence or potency could be improved by raising the general physical and mental condition through yoga. Good health, emotional and nervous stability and a well-functioning endocrinal system are all essential to a satisfactory sex life.

The traditional hatha yoga texts place great emphasis on delaying age and prolonging life. Time must be held back to give the yogi every opportunity to reach his highest state of development, mental and spiritual, to master the techniques that lead to *samadhi*. The great benefits of these practices to circulation, digestion, nerves, joints, muscles, organs, glands and general confidence are now widely recognized in the West. In particular, certain *asanas,* (bodily positions) have been found to have direct bearing on both male and female reproductive systems. It is a strange fact that certain poses designed for celibate yogis could benefit non-celibate men and women and promote sexual vitality. The physiological effect is entirely influenced by the mode of concentration.

Other features of training—correct breathing, knowledge of relaxation, preservation of and recharging with vital energy—are indispensable in maintaining sexual youth and vigour.

Nor are these benefits limited to improvement of sex life. All over the world, we are now more harassed, tense and uneasy than ever before. The speed of modern life threatens to run us down, our own inventions to destroy us, hatred and distrust confront us on every side.

Into this chaos, yoga brings its message of peace and sanity, a message we cannot afford to ignore.

The Path of Celibacy

Wandering ascetics. True and false yogis. Aims of celibate and ascetic yogis. Discipline in *ashrams*. The *cakras*. The vital energies. Sublimation. Techniques and exercises.

The figure of the celibate monk, the wandering ascetic, the hermit who has renounced the flesh has always impressed, astonished, fascinated, shocked, even outraged the worldly man. Only the simplest, most unspoilt natures lack the human tendency to question powers in others that we do not possess ourselves; yet the true ascetic who lives by his beliefs must command respect from the most cynical and materialistic householder.

In the East, particularly in India, countless so-called holy men, mud-smeared, daubed with ashes or dung, with matted hair, sometimes naked, sometimes grotesquely mutilated, are seen wandering, or seated by the roadside, with their begging bowls. Some never speak; others have grown arrogant, demanding food, claiming every privilege as the right of a *saddhu*. For the most part the population accept and even revere them; yet many are little more than professional beggars, without scruples, restraint or spiritual purpose. Their freedom from worldly ties and possessions comes less from renunciation than shiftlessness, laziness, even stupidity.

A book written some seventy years ago (C. J. Oman's *Indian Life, Religious and Social*) quotes two accounts of these *saddhus,* recorded at different times. A 9th-century Moslem historian, Abu Zaid, described men who wandered in woods and mountains, rarely speaking, living on herbs and forest fruit, often naked. Others, wearing only a panther skin, stood for long periods with their faces turned to the sun. One such man was found sixteen years later, in the same position, to the writer's astonishment.

The second account, written hundreds of years later, is of 'one of the celebrated yoghees, who was lying in the sun in the street, the nails of whose hands were grown into his cheek, and a bird's nest on his head'. When asked 'How can one obtain the knowledge of God?' he replied, 'Do not ask me questions. You may look at me, for I am God.'

The true ascetic yogi is not found standing by the roadside on one leg or sitting on beds of nails for public edification. His life is ruled by rigid discipline. He works unceasingly to achieve self-mastery, to suppress his worldly and sensual instincts, or transmute them into a means of attaining the goal of yoga—immortality and freedom. His practice is done in private, in *ashrams* or monasteries, in remote caves or forests. He is indeed a holy man, dedicated to God, his life an unceasing attempt to become more spirit than flesh . . . 'winning the chaste mind even in sleep, even while . . . in the prime of life,' as St Augustine longed to do.

The early Christians' methods of subduing the flesh, though often differing in practice from yoga, were founded on the same aspiration. In East and West there is a long history of man's struggles to turn sexual desire into spiritual strength by drastic physical measures. Even emasculation was not unusual. In India, China, the Middle East, Russia, thousands maimed and tortured themselves in attempts to destroy the 'serpent of desire'. Monks spent sleepless nights praying and reading holy scripts lest the devil, disguised as a beautiful woman, visit their dreams. 'The devil is clever and cunning,' wrote a medieval monk, 'he can assume many forms, as horrible as a spectre from the pit of hell; but he is most dangerous not when he comes with hoofs and horns, but like a beautiful naked woman, all tenderness and desire.'

In Tolstoy's dramatic story, *Father Sergei,* a celibate monk-hermit, tempted by a beautiful woman, chopped off his index finger to drive out desire by shock and pain. The western saints and mystics who observed long exhausting fasts, wore coarse hair shirts or heavy chains,

slept in sitting, even kneeling positions were motivated by
the same idea . . . to kill one form of torment with another. They were breaking the body, mortifying the flesh;
but though an effective tool for the purpose this method
often led to untold misery, premature ageing, disease and
untimely death.

To the yogi who regards his body as the temple and
vessel of the spirit, such abuses are inadmissible. Though
the celibate seeker's life may be austere and demanding,
the body is always respected.

In general, suppressive practices are more common
among primitive ascetics. The more intellectual schools of
yoga believe in *utilizing* sexual energy by sublimation or
transmutation into other forms of energy.

Suppression and sublimation have somewhat different
meanings in yoga (or in religion) and in worldly life. The
yogi, or the man of religion, *voluntarily* suppresses or
sublimates for a specific purpose; but no normal man or
woman with normal sex instincts willingly deprives themselves of this natural part of life. For them, the usual
causes of celibacy are factors beyond control . . . poor
health; ignorance; fear; social, economic, even sentimental reasons. The effects vary with the strength of the individual's sex urge. In some, it may be so weak that abstinence gives rise to little inconvenience; in others, it could
provide ceaseless torment, or, though outwardly overcome, turn malignant, manifesting in hatred, bigotry, mil-
itant puritanism, even perversions.

Though sublimation is preferable to suppression, it is
no easy alternative. It is an intensely difficult psychic and
physical process which, as Havelock Ellis said, is 'far easier to talk about than achieve.' There are exceptions.
Many great artists have possessed strong passions and
sexual drive, and it is often suggested that their creative
achievements resulted from conscious or unconscious
sublimation of sex. Tolstoy, author of *War and Peace,*
once told a friend, wringing his hands, 'Oh, if I could
only be free from desire for three hours . . . how much
more I could create!'; but such cases are rare. For the
majority, sublimation is far more likely to be some kind
of substitution. For the fortunate it could take a harmless
and beneficial form . . . helping others, social services,

constructive activities. Less happy manifestations are neuroses, hypochondria or varying obsessions.

SUPPRESSION, SUBLIMATION AND TRANSMUTATION OF SEX ENERGY IN YOGA PRACTICE

Sexual desire, in its lowest animal form, keeps the human mind tied to the earth, prevents it soaring to higher planes of consciousness. There are those who believe that the spirit is liberated after discharge of sexual tension; artists have claimed that the greatest creative inspiration comes immediately after intercourse, when completely freed of desire; but most mystical schools, including ascetic yoga, hold that loss of semen is destructive to mental powers, that sexual energy should be transmuted to energy of the mind. It is taught that by retention of semen (*bindu*) a yogi becomes strong and beautiful as a god, develops miraculous powers and overcomes death. Seminal energy retained in the body is directed to the brain, where it manifests not only as psychic gifts and greater control of concentration but as *ojas,* the subtle, indefinable power of command and personal magnetism.

Although, physiologically, brain, sex organs and spinal cord are so interdependent that the sexologist Wilhelm Stekel defined impotence as a struggle between brain and spinal cord, it should be mentioned here that the words *seed, bindu, sperm,* etc., are used metaphorically as well as literally.

The texts state repeatedly that he who can give 'upward flow' to the seed is a god; the value of retained *bindu* is mentioned again and again. The Nath yogis, who practised sexual techniques with women for liberation, (retaining their *bindu*), regard woman as the archenemy, the destroyer of man's strength. She is a serpent, a hypocrite cat; an enchantress by day and a tigress by night, for she seeks the man's seed. Charmed and allured by her, he loses his vital energy.

In one of the Nath legends the yogini Mahanamati tells her son: 'All men serve women gratis; the *maha-rasa* within the body is worth 1000s of chests filled with gems; and when that wealth is lost man becomes subdued by a

woman. A lioness is she and casts her eyes like a tigress.
She leaves aside the bones and flesh and sucks up the
maha-rasa. Woman deals in the wealth of man and the
allured man goes on serving her gratis. With his plough
and bulls man cultivates the field of others . . . there is
the loss of the bulls and of the seed into the bargain.'

Conservation of *bindu* or seminal energy leads also to
development of higher faculties in Rajah and Kundalini
yoga. It is said that these powers* . . . telepathy, clairvoy-
ance, universal memory, etc. . . . are dormant in all men.
Occasionally they are fully developed at birth—as in
mathematical 'freaks', mind-readers, mediums, but for the
most part are rarely awakened. It is held that we are not
yet enlightened enough to enjoy them but that eventually
they will be the common property of mankind. But
though we are not yet ready to read each other's minds,
'chosen ones' could develop supra-human powers by certain techniques and methods, aided by *bramacharya* (celibate life) and the transmutation of sexual energy into
power of the mind.

In yoga, special techniques are employed for suppression and sublimation, for transmuting bodily energies into
spiritual force, but before these can be mentioned, two
important aspects of teaching must be understood. These
concern the different Energies and the system of *Cakras*
(pronounced chakra) in the subtle-physical body.

THE FIVE ENERGIES

The texts list ten vital energies in the body, but we are
concerned here with the main five: physical; mental; sexual; energy of intellect; energy of soul. The last two are
independent and cannot be transmuted. Since energy of
the soul, the divine spark, is part of universal energy, it is
also indestructible. The first three energies are inter-

---

* The *Siddhis* or Attainments (supra-human powers) result from
conquering the laws of nature by training and discipline. They include thirty-eight physical and eight spiritual *siddhis* . . . ability to
see infinitely small or infinitely large things; to defy gravity; to control
the elements; knowledge of past, present and future; freedom from
hunger and thirst, etc. Many of the 'physical' feats are not necessarily
to be interpreted literally but symbolize inner powers.

changeable or transmutable. Sexual energy, (conscious and unconscious desire) could therefore be transformed into either physical energy or energy of the mind.

The seat of physical energy—known as Mother of Energies, or Sun Energy—is the solar-plexus. Sexual energy (Moon Energy) is in the region of the sex organs (Moon region). The head, (*Brahmahcakra, Sahasrara,* the Thousand-petalled Lotus) is the seat of mental energy.

THE CAKRAS

The *cakras* (literally, wheel, circle) are centres or 'junctions' of *nadis,* nervous channels of the physical-subtle body.

Among the *nadis* (72,000) *three* are considered the most important: *sushumna*—within the spinal column; *Ida;* and *Pingala.* These last two start in the left and right nostrils respectively, move up to the crown of the head and course downwards to the base of the spine. They intersect and also cross *sushumna* in their passage through the body.

An Indian doctor of medicine who investigated yogic physical controls has suggested that '*Ida* and *Pingala* correspond to gangliated cords of the sympathetic nervous system, situated on either side of the spine.'*

There are six main *cakras* (the seventh is the Thousand-petalled Lotus in the top of the head). Traditional literature describes each one and its 'awakening'. (This is the purpose of Kundalini yoga, the method of developing supra-human powers.) As the coiled serpent Kundalini makes her upward journey . . . having been roused by appropriate practices . . . she becomes connected with the different *cakras* and eventually with the brain itself. The gradual 'illumination' of each *cakra* brings to life a different attainment, both on physical and mental planes.

Siva Samhita, a technical treatise on Hatha and Rajah yoga, describes the *cakras* in the symbolic language so typical of the ancient texts. This was used with deliberate intent to confuse, in order to protect the secret teachings

---

* Rele, V. G.: *The Mysterious Kundalini.*

from the unworthy. It could only be understood with the
help of a *guru*.

The first, at the base of the spine, is *Muladhara cakra*,
the Root Centre, lying above the anus, below the root of
the penis. 'This is the Root lotus of which *yoni* is the
heart. The centre is most resplendent, with four petals
bearing four characters . . .'

This *cakra* is yellow, and its four petals are red. They
are the four aspects of the vital breath and are linked
with Kundalini, the Coiled Energy, which lies at the
base of the spinal cord. On the four petals are golden
characters, representing aspects of Kundalini as she lies
sleeping. In the centre of *Muladhara* is the magic character 'Lang' carried on the elephant Airavata. From *Muladhara, sushumna* begins.

Above *Muladhara,* (the Root *cakra*), is *Svadhishthana
cakra,* 'Support of the Life Breath.' It is white in colour,
has six red petals bearing the characters B, Bh, M, Y, R,
L. 'There dwells the Realized Being called the Arrow . . .
The Presiding Deity is Rakini'.

It is said that this centre is connected with the sense of
taste, the organ of action (hand) and the phenomenon of
contraction.

The third *cakra* is *Manipura,* Lotus of the Navel, in the
solar-plexus area, the seat of physical energy. 'The seeker
who ever meditates on this *cakra* gains the *Patala* attainment, giver of all other attainments. Pain and disease are
destroyed, all desires fulfilled and Time defeated. The
Seeker can enter into the bodies of others, he has the
power of making gold . . . he knows medicinal plants and
can discover treasures.'

Next on the upward journey to the head is *Anahata
cakra,* the Centre of the Unstruck Sound. Set in the centre of the chest (in the heart region), it has twelve petals
of 'flaming red', bearing numbers or characters. 'This is
the place where dwells in delight the Seed of Wind . . .'
(It is the springing place of the vital breath.) Some writers associate this centre, anatomically, with the cardiac
plexus. Meditation upon *Anahata* brings auspicious results in this and other worlds.

The fifth *cakra, Vishuddha,* is the Centre of Great Purity and is set in the pharyngeal region. One who medi-

tates upon this centre, the door of liberation, obtains knowledge of past, present and future, becomes a scholar of the secret knowledge and a Prince among Yogis.

Ajna cakra is situated between the eyebrows and is known as the Centre of Command. It has two petals and its colour is white. Through concentration on *Ajna cakra* Supreme Realization is attained.

Brahmahcakra, (*Sahasrara*) the Lotus of 1,000 Petals, controls all, for it is the mind; yet according to the teachings this in itself is only one-fifth developed.

CELIBATE PRACTICES

Sexual desire, whether conscious or subconscious, is a distracting power that must be controlled. When *suppressed* it increases power of concentration; by *sublimation* it increases also the power of the mind.

Yogis and mystics have practices both for suppression and sublimation. Some are mentioned in the *sutras,* others are preserved by mouth-to-ear tradition from teachers to *chelas* in *ashrams*.

There are numerous ways of suppressing sexual energy: hard work during the day, meditation, exercise and prayer; studying scripts and reading of holy books; long discussion 'at the feet of the Master', singing *mantras* and practice of certain bodily poses.

Sublimation involves special techniques where pose, breath and concentration are combined in one powerful effort.

In some of the *ashrams* of India, Tibet and China, when a disciple is accepted, he is usually told that for the following nine months he must keep all his seminal fluid intact. His horoscope is studied for the position of his birth planet in relation to the full moon (sexual energy is the Moon Energy). Even his sleep, on certain nights, is watched, so that he may be woken if erotic dreams threaten a loss of semen.

Twice daily, sublimative exercises are practised. To help the disciple in his training, *mantrums* and *mandalas* are given to stabilize the mind. Food is carefully selected ... (garlic, onions, pepper, paprika and curry are forbidden). Breath control is practised four times a day: at dawn, midday, sunset and midnight, leaving little time for sleep. On waking in the morning stretching movements must be practised, then the disciple must get up at once. (The bed is narrow, hard, without mattress . . . boards covered with a blanket, the pillow small and flat.)

The morning is very active. Six purifications are practised; the bowels must be emptied, with contractions of the stomach (*Uddiyana* and *Nauli*) before and during the act to ensure complete evacuation; this is followed by thorough cleaning and washing of the rectum. The face and mouth are washed, the teeth cleaned, nostrils washed, gums massaged and tongue scraped of impurities.

A small amount of water, or fruit juice when available, is taken. Though not a traditional practice for suppressing desire, some teachers suggest fifteen to twenty slow squatting movements over a basin of cool water, keeping the feet flat, immersing the genitals with each movement.

The relationship between *guru* and *chela* (teacher and disciple) is that of a wise father and loving son. There are no secrets, no false modesty between them and every human problem is discussed openly and straight-forwardly.

If the teacher learns that his charge is uneasy through desire, before and after morning practice he is given the *Pose of an Eagle* (plate 17, in insert) and the *Pose of a Tree* (plate 16, in insert) which he must hold for a considerable time. In the first pose, due to the position of the legs (one wound round the other) pressure is placed in the sex organs. Combined with deep breathing and concentration, this pose gives the required results.

In the *Pose of a Tree,* the mind is concentrated on inner tranquillity, leaving no place for any other thought.

The surrounding location, the very atmosphere of the *ashrams* devoted to *brahmacharya* (celibacy) help the seeker to achieve his goal. These hermitages are in secluded places, high up in the mountains, in a dense forest, or, in some parts of China, on tiny islands.

Life is strictly regimented; the number of disciples is small. At one *ashram* Michael Volin met a seventy-year-old yogi who had never seen a woman in his life. He had been brought to the hermitage as a child of two, orphaned in one of the countless local skirmishes, and had never once left its grounds. All the forces of his being had been transmuted into calm power of the mind.

SUPPRESSION

If *suppression* of desire is analyzed it will be found to consist of persistent continuous diversion of mental processes into channels that are completely disassociated from every aspect of sexual activity. Mental exercises that lead to control of thoughts, or sorting 'seeds of thought', must be practised.

CONTROL OF THOUGHTS

Sitting in one of the cross-legged positions, with slow rhythmical breathing established, the student gradually removes every thought from the mind, one by one, eventually achieving complete stillness.

SORTING SEEDS OF THOUGHT

Thought starts in impulse, in yoga called 'seed' of thought.

After pose and breath are established, these seeds are analysed . . . 'fertilizing the positive and rooting out the negative.'

DEVELOPMENT OF INNER STRENGTH

This is a regular suppressive exercise, practised either in cross-legged position or *Pose of a Hero* (plate 12, in insert).

In the first, sit with legs crossed, hands clasped, fingers interlocked. Establish deep and rhythmical breath and concentrate on the thought of developing inner strength.

This, of course, has nothing to do with physical strength. It could be perhaps described as moral strength

. . . the ability to act honourably in the crises of life, to fulfil one's own resolutions.

SUBLIMATION OF SEXUAL ENERGY

This practice is not confined to ascetic yogis. As already mentioned, a number of advanced techniques of Kundalini and Rajah yoga demand the concentration of *all energies*. Kundalini, the 'sleeping serpent', can only be roused by an increased effort of will-mind, generating extra energy. This extra energy is drawn from sublimated sex.

Sublimative techniques are based on the principle that physical, sexual and mental energies are inter-changeable. (page 16) Mental energy is the master, commanding all other energies.

The transmutation of physical and sexual energy to that of the mind is achieved by combined thought and breath, supported by certain *asanas*.

These practices are done in secret, known only to the *guru,* but even he is not present when they are performed. They are usually carried out in a small room, practically bare of furniture, on a comfortable mat used for *asana* practice. It is essential that there are no disturbing influences or interruptions.

'Retire to a solitary place, such as a mountain cave or a sacred spot. The place must be protected from the wind and rain, and it must have a smooth, clean floor, free from pebbles and dust. It must not be damp, and it must be free from disturbing noises. It must be pleasing to the eye and quietening to the mind.'*

The actual technique of sublimation includes the art of *Full Breath of a Yogi;* the study of different *asanas* or bodily poses; and the Power of Concentration. As in many yoga practices this is a three-fold effort, and each of the three components must be mastered.

FULL BREATH OF A YOGI

Through this technique an extra amount of *prana* (cosmic energy, life force—see Glossary), is inhaled with

---

* *The Upanishads:* Prabhavananda and Manchester. trs.

each breath. At the same time the blood-stream is more efficiently purified by increased intake of oxygen.

In *Full Breath of a Yogi* inhalation starts with the downward movement of the diaphragm, causing a slight protrusion of the stomach (as though inflating). By this movement the bottom of the lungs are filled; then the middle part is filled; finally, the top of the lungs are inflated to complete the breath.

It is taught that one who gains complete control of breath eventually gains complete control of life force, cosmic energy or *prana*.

The main positions for sublimative or suppressive techniques are:

PROSTRATE POSE

   Savasana

SITTING POSES

   Easy pose
   Pose of attainment (*Siddhasana*—pose of an Adept)
   Half-lotus
   Full lotus
   Diamond Pose
   Bound Lotus
   Frog pose
   Hero pose
   Dangerous pose

INVERTED POSES

   Shoulderstand
   Inverted gesture (Half shoulderstand)
   Pose of Tranquillity
   Bound Shoulderstand
   Headstand, with variations
   Bound headstand; Inverted Eagle; Pagoda position.

OTHER POSES, such as

> Mountain pose
> Knee-foot pose
> Hidden *padmasana*
> And certain *mudras:*
>> *Aswini-mudra; yoga-mudra; vajroli-mudra; yoni-mudra, maha-mudra* (See plate 32, in insert)

POSE OF *Savasana*

Mastery of *Savasana,* or Pose of Complete Rest, gives victory over tiredness and enables the disciple to replenish physical energy in a very short time. Sublimative practices are often done in this position.

The pose has four stages:

1. Muscles are completely relaxed.
2. This is followed by withdrawal of inner tension. (This withdrawal involves a method known as 'inverted Mind's Eye' . . . the ability to look into the body).
3. Deep and rhythmical breath is then established, filling the *nadis* with *prana;*

and 4. in the final stage the disciple performs 'Small Exit from the Physical Body', entering his own spiritual *ashram* . . . a beautiful garden created by his mind.

When *Savasana* is combined with sublimative practices, the fourth stage—Small Exit—is not completed. The yogi, with body completely relaxed, deeply breathing, uses pranic energy to move sexual energy up along *sushumna* to *Manipura cakra* (solar-plexus) or to *Brahmahcakra,* in the head. The incoming breath draws on the moon or sex energy; (see page 17); the outgoing breath sends it to the desired *cakra.*

As soon as sex energy leaves its customary seat it ceases to be specifically sexual. It becomes pure energy, acquiring either physical or mental properties on reaching the corresponding *cakras*.

Dissolving of sexual energy is often performed by celibate yogis in *Savasana*. After pose and breath are established, concentrate on the seat of sexual energy, (the reproductive organs). With *exhalation* this energy is 'dissolved', breathed out of the body.

SITTING POSES

Easy pose. Sitting in Easy Pose (simple crosslegged position) with back and neck in one straight line (this is very important), establish slow rhythmical breath. (The ratio is usually six heart-beats or units for inhalation, six for exhalation). With incoming breath, sex energy is drawn or moved from its seat; with outgoing breath it is directed to *Manipura* or to *Brahmahcakra*.

Pose of an Adept. (*Siddhasana*) (Page 127). *Siddhasana,* 'Opener of the door of salvation' is used in *ashrams* for sublimative purposes. It is thus described in the traditional texts:

'Press firmly the heel of the left foot against the perineum, and the right heel above the male organ. With the chin pressing on the chest one should sit tight, having restrained the senses.'

In a variation of the pose, commonly used for sublimation, the left heel is placed above the male organ and the right heel upon it.

Back and neck are held in a straight line, the eyes are closed and after breath is established the same technique as in Easy Pose is employed.

Lotus position. (*Padmasana*) In suppressive techniques for preventing accumulation of the sex urge the feet should be locked in *padmasana* (page 125) and so arranged that the heels effect pressure on penis and testicles. Breath and concentration are as in previous crosslegged poses.

(English writers of the last century referred to these poses as disgusting and indecent.)

Variation. To increase the suppressive power of this pose, the closed fists are pressed against the body in the region of the groin and the forehead brought down to the floor while deeply breathing. The *chela* (disciple) concentrates upon 'banishing desire from the body'.

Bound Lotus. (See page 126). In this further variation, arms as well as legs are locked. The power of the pose is thus increased to the state where a 'disembodied' sensation is felt. *Half-lotus pose.* Only one leg is locked at a time (see plate 11, in insert). Breathing and concentration are as in *Full Lotus.*

Diamond Pose * and *Pose of a Frog* (plate 13, in insert) are also used in sublimative exercises as giving variety of position. In all, the technique is as described above, a combination of breath and concentration. *Pose of a Frog* is often recommended to celibate yoginis (female yogis), combined with meditation upon the theme 'My body is open, but only the ether possesses me'.

Dangerous Pose is used for both suppression and sublimation, and should be practised under direction of the *guru.*

Sitting on the floor, on a comfortable mat or folded blanket, place the legs so that left heel is alongside the right thigh, and the right heel alongside the left. (See plate 15). The thighs are interlocked, effecting pressure on the genital organs. The palms of the hands rest on the top knee which is placed above the other so that both are in line. Breath is established and the mind either concentrated upon complete suppression, or on the thought of moving sexual energy from its customary seat, by way of *sushumna,* up to the solar plexus (*Manipura cakra*) or the head (*Brahmahcakra*).

INVERTED POSES

These are the most favoured for sublimation. Reversing the force of gravitational pull assists the process. Numerous inverted poses are used for this purpose. They must first be mastered to perfection so the practitioner could completely concentrate without distraction.

---

* Sitting back on heels, legs together, hands resting on knees. Back and neck in one straight line.

Sarvangasana (*Shoulderstand*). In a small well-ventilated room, without draught or any possible interruption and after preparing a comfortable mat, lie down on the back and slowly, in one continuous movement, raise legs and body till they form a straight line with the chin tightly pressed to the chest. The eyes are then closed and breath established. The 'moon region' is now above *Manipura* and *Brahmahcakra*. With inhalation sexual energy is drawn from its seat, with exhalation directed through the spinal cord *downwards*.

Concentrate on the seat of sexual energy, in the region of the sex organs. With *inhalation,* imagine that you are drawing on that energy; with *exhalation* that you are directing it through *sushumna* upon its journey to *Manipura cakra* (solar plexus, seat of physical energy).

This must be practised for a considerable time, until there is the feeling that all sexual energy has been drained from its customary seat and transmuted to the centre of physical energy. The sensation is described as a remarkable uplift of physical power and a 'beautiful, contented' relief from sexual desire.

If this physical energy is to be transmuted into 'calm power of the mind' the same method is used again . . . with inhalation drawing on the physical energy, with exhalation directing it by *sushumna nadi* to the *Brahmahcakra* or 1,000-petalled lotus of the mind.

The texts advise holding this and the following pose until a sweet taste is experienced on the tip of the tongue. (The mouth should first be thoroughly cleansed.) This is the 'nectar of the 1,000-petalled lotus' and indicates that actual sublimation has taken place. Some *gurus* advise the 'inverted position of the tongue'—the tip of the tongue pressed to the roof of the mouth.

Bound Shoulderstand. (See plate 5, in insert). To increase the effect of the pose, the legs may be interlocked, in the Lotus seat. Breathing and concentration are as in *Sarvangasana*.

The pose is completed by bringing the still-locked legs slowly down, over the head, pressing the heels against the lower part of the stomach as a final touch.

Balancing Shoulderstand. (See plate 7, in insert). This is very similar to *Sarvangasana*. It has all the advantages of the latter, as well as an increased flow of blood to the head, due to the raised arms. The breathing and concentration are as in *Sarvangasana*.

Triangular Pose, or Pose of Tranquillity, (Plate 3) is also used, with the same breathing and concentration.

Head pose. (Plate 8). This is the most powerful of all inverted poses, for sublimative purposes. It affects the entire body and great caution must be exercised in practice.

In the early stages it must not be held for more than half a minute. *Only after intense purification and bodily training can it be safely held for any great length of time.* Prolonged periods are not for ordinary students.

With the Moon region now above *Manipura* and *Brahmahcakra,* as in other inverted positions, sexual energy is transmuted by combined deep breathing and concentration. Variations in the position of the legs increase the power of the pose.

Bound headstand (Oordhva padmasana . . . Inverted Lotus). The legs are locked in the lotus position during the headstand. This may be done by two different methods. If the hips are supple enough, the ordinary headstand or 'skull gesture' is practised, then the legs locked into the Lotus position while still on the head. (Page 125). The second method is to lock the legs first, while sitting on the floor, then come into the headstand.

The combination of inverted pose and pressure of feet against the groin speeds up the sublimation process. Breathing and concentration are as in ordinary headstand: with *inhalation* the mind concentrates on the thought of drawing sex energy from its usual seat; with *exhalation* the energy is directed to either *Manipura* or *Brahmahcakra*.

In celibate practice the genital organs are actually locked between the heels, and the mind is concentrated on *suppression* of desire.

Inverted Eagle. While holding the Head pose the legs are twisted into the Eagle position (plate 9, in insert). The genital organs are thus squeezed between the thighs, while breath and concentration are practised as in Inverted *padmasana*. When sublimation is desired the mind concentrates on sublimation; when suppression is the objective this is the focus for concentration.

Inverted pagoda. In the Head Pose, join the soles of the feet together and lower them, with knees apart, as directed on page 124. See also *Inverted Tree,* (plate 10).

In some schools these poses are practised by celibate yoginis (female yogis) and meditation is upon the theme . . . *Body open to the ether, pure and devoid of passion.*

Knee-foot pose. (See plate 18). This pose, described on page 130, is used by some celibate yogis for suppressive exercises. It is demanding and difficult and prolonged practice is usually exhausting. Performed on both left and right side, it supports the usual breath-concentration by the pressure of the heels in the groin.

Mountain pose. Used for the same purpose. (See page 131) The position of the legs—locked in the Lotus position—brings the heels into the groins where they exert pressure. The pose, which involves standing balanced on the knees while legs are locked, is difficult and in prolonged practice a meditative stick is used for support.

Hidden padmasana. With legs locked in *padmasana* the yogi lies on his stomach, deeply inhaling and exhaling, concentrating on mastery of desire. (Plate 29, in insert). The prone position increases the pressure of the heels against the groins.

MUDRAS

Asanas should always be learnt from a teacher, particularly in sublimative and suppressive techniques. Only the *guru* can advise which should be practised, how long they should be held and so on.

This is specially important in the case of *mudras,* which if misinterpreted or misapplied could cause serious injury. For this reason the most important *mudras* are referred to in the texts as 'secret', 'most secret', or 'secret of secrets', and described in a confusing manner that must be clarified by the *guru.*

Among the *mudras* used for sublimation and suppression are *yoga-mudra; aswini-mudra; vajroli-mudra,* and *yoni-mudra.* The first two, being comparatively simple, are described on page 128. *Vajroli* and *yoni-mudra,* which are among the 'most secret' are included in Chapter 3—The Tantric Path—in their original cryptic descriptions. For *maha-mudra*, see page 137.

Vajroli-mudra, the Thunderbolt Gesture that destroys the darkness of the world, and must be kept the 'secret of secrets', is the technique of completely controlling the movement of semen. *Yoni-mudra* is the contraction of the *yoni* place (perineum) behind the male organ. Though both these *mudras* are used to control semen during intercourse they are also used as sublimative techniques.

Vajroli-mudra practised in combination with *Khechari-mudra* is said to give great powers, to conquer death, to make the yogi beautiful as a god of love. In preparation for *Khechari* the tongue is loosened from the floor of the mouth by cutting the frenum, and lengthened by 'milking' (pulling it out) over a period of time—(6 months). In the *mudra* it is turned up and back until it blocks off the entrance of the nasal passage into the mouth. With breath thus sealed up in the body, thought suspended and semen arrested in *vajroli-mudra* the yogi's psychomental powers are greatly increased and he achieves liberation.

'He who practises *Khechari,* his tongue in the hole above the glottis, and whose seed does not flow even in the embrace of a desirable woman, who keeps his seed in his body, what fear has he of death? So long as the Gesture of the Void is held, so long the seed cannot fall. If the seed happen to fall, then, when it reaches the womb it is drawn up again forcibly by the power of the *yoni-mudra*.'

All these techniques and mudras may only be learnt from a guru.

The Tantric Path

Purpose and meaning of the Tantras. Tantric teachings. The path of Desire. Tantric practices. Intercourse as a ritual. Yogic-sexual techniques used in Tantrism. Later cults developing out of Tantrism. Buddhist and Vaisnava *Sahajayists*.

THE PURPOSE OF TANTRISM

To understand the purpose of Tantric practices it is necessary to know the thought behind them.

The goal of 'classical' yoga is to unite the individual Self (*Atman*) with the Universal Self (*Brahman*) in the superconscious state known as *samadhi*. In *samadhi* there is only pure Being. Duality is abolished; all is unified, merged, identified.

Though the Tantrics employ different names and different terms, their purpose is the same: union; non-duality; mergence.

Before Creation there was unity, non-duality. Creation broke this unity; non-duality became duality. Man, as part of Creation, is dualistic. He thinks in terms of subject-object, can only exist *in relation to*—to time, other people, surroundings. This is the cause of his suffering and bondage for in his dualistic, relative state he is influenced by the world, exposed to events and circumstances he cannot control. Only through a return to the primal unity (non-duality) can he know the freedom of pure Being.

The desire for this freedom is the motive behind Tantric practices—as behind all yoga. Whether achieved within the disciple's own body, or through the union of two bodies, the goal is always the reunification of the two principles separated at the time of Creation.

According to the school, sect, or cult these two principles may be known as positive-negative, static-dynamic, male-female, seed-ovum, action-inaction, pure consciousness-cosmic energy, Void-Compassion, Wisdom-Means, Sakti-Siva, Krishna-Radha, *Yab-Yum* (father-mother), etc. . . . When united they bring the state of suspension in which pure Being is experienced. One who has known it is 'liberated in life'. Earthly existence holds no terrors for him.

We have seen how the ascetic achieves liberation within his own body by disciplining mind, will-power and energy, sublimating and transmuting even sexual energy for this purpose; but there are other methods. Members of some hatha yoga sects, certain Tantric schools and cults developing out of Tantrism believe that super-consciousness is attained through yogic sexual techniques involving coitus.*

A Tantric yogi is one who seeks liberation through the teaching of the Tantras or Tantric *shastras,* (religious scriptures), also known as *Agamas* or Revelations.

Though scholars dispute their age and origin, the traditional belief is that they were revealed by the god Siva, through Sakti, his consort, the Divine Mother.

Human history falls into four ages; the *Satya yuga, Treta yuga, Dvapara yuga* and *Kali yuga.* Each age needed a religious scripture for help and guidance. For the *Satya yuga*—known as the Golden Age—there were the Vedas, the oldest books in the world. The men of this time were physical and spiritual giants, beautiful, immensely strong and long-lived. They were full of goodness, compassion, honour, nobility, generosity, purity and happiness. Endowed with great physical and spiritual power and control they could observe the high ideals, celibacy and other austerities imposed by the Vedas.

In the *Treta yuga,* though strength, virtue, beauty, longevity had decreased by a quarter it was still possible, with some difficulty, to follow the Vedic path; but the

---

* Contrary to popular belief, · many Tantric schools are ascetic. The sexual practices which gained notoriety for Tantrism were practised only by certain sects and cults, and even here they were often abused and misinterpreted.

Dvapara yuga brought an even greater decline. Men were now only half the size of their *Satya* ancestors; virtue was reduced by one half, longevity by nine-tenths. Increasingly swayed by greed, avarice, anger, lust, envy, people were neither physically nor spiritually capable of obeying the Vedic teachings. A modified form was evolved by sages as suitable for *Dvapara* man; but even this was too demanding for the *Kali yuga* (the Dark Age) in which we now live. Compared to the supermen of the Golden Age we are pygmies, dominated by base instincts, lacking in moral strength, virtue, nobility; physical and spiritual weaklings, whose lives are too short for any hope of salvation by the austere way.

Seeing the plight into which mankind had fallen, Sakti, the Divine Mother, appealed to her lord Siva for a Scripture suited to the *Kali* man's limitations, which could help and guide him to liberation.

'Oh Lord! graciously tell me the means by which men may acquire long life, health, strength, vigour and manliness; . . . endowed with great strength and courage . . . pure-minded, benevolent, . . . faithful to their wives . . . lovers of God . . .'

Siva then expounded the Tantras, as the scriptures for the Dark Age.

One of the impediments to *Kali yuga* man's spiritual progress is his intellectual development. This cleverness, manifested in scientific and technical achievements, has confused his sense of values, led him to take the unreal for the real, to cling to the things of this world. Such an attitude, contrary to all Vedic teachings, at once disqualifies him for this path; but the Tantras make allowances for human shortcomings, providing a system of spiritual training suited for each individual nature.

'She (the Divine Mother) does not exact from her weak and short-lived children of the *Kali yuga* long and trying *Brahmacharya* (celibacy) and austerity to show them the way to her Lotus Feet . . . The low and the high, all are equally taken care of, and for all, the path has been made smooth and straight.' *

---

* It is believed that at the end of our dark age the *Kalki Avatara* —Rider on the White Horse—will come to destroy evil and restore the rule of righteousness.

It is often said that the inner teaching of the Tantras is as old as the Vedas, that Tantrism was an ancient Indian cult which now appeared in a new outward form. At all events it became enormously popular from about the 4th century onward, among both Hindus and Buddhists. In its later days, through abuse and misinterpretation, it fell into disrepute, degenerating into decadent and orgiastic cults which made the name Tantric synonymous with every kind of erotic and sensual excess.

The popularity of the new philosophy is easily understood. Pre-Tantric man, trained to believe the world an evil illusion, yet unable to liberate himself by the austere Vedic path, had fallen into a no-man's-land of despair. Tantrism brought comfort and hope with its teaching that the world was neither evil nor an illusion, that it was a manifestation of the Divine Mother and therefore supreme goodness; that by identifying himself with this supreme goodness man could raise himself towards perfection, could even in one life attain a state of spiritual development that might take an ascetic many incarnations to achieve. 'Tantrism uses the power of Nature, human passions and instincts, to conquer, with their aid, the world of the senses. This way leads from the physical to the abstract . . . This is the way of the mystic and also the lefthand way, which may utilize even eroticism and drunkenness as means of spiritual achievement.'

'This way can be dangerous but may bring quick and wonderful results; according to the Tantra it is the only method of bringing actual results in this Age of Strife (*Kali yuga*). Ascetics take several lives to reach God by the righthand path, which is too slow a rate of spiritual progress. Passion alone, when astutely directed, can overcome egotism and pride and calculation . . . it alone has the momentum to draw man away from the bonds chaining him to interest, beliefs, virtues, reputation . . .' *

TANTRIC TEACHINGS

It was inevitable that the Tantras should be misinterpreted since they teach that spiritual advancement is best

---

* Danielou, Alain: *Hindu Polytheism*.

achieved by means of those very things which are the
cause of man's downfall; that 'through enjoyment one
gains liberation; for enjoyment is the means of reaching
the Supreme Abode. Hence the wise who wish to conquer
. . . should experience all pleasure.' *

The most important quality in any act is the spirit in
which it is performed; the motive behind it. Motive can
transform a physical act to a sacrament, just as when the
inner meaning is abandoned or forgotten the act becomes
at best meaningless, at worst harmful or degrading. The
motive behind the Tantric teaching was wise and realis-
tic: a thing forbidden gains added strength and attraction;
but enjoyed to the point of satiety, it will be voluntarily
discarded in favour of something better. Even acts that,
according to the Tantras send men to hell, are permitted
for the purpose of divesting them of their attractions . . .
of 'getting them out of the system' . . . as controlled
doses of poison are given for therapeutic purposes.

'With the very poison, a little of which would kill any
other being, a man who understands poison would dispel
another poison . . . so existence is purified by existence
in the countering of discursive thought by its own kind.
Those who have been burned by the fire of passion, must
suffer the fire of passion. Those things by which men of
evil conduct are bound, others turn into means and gain
thereby release from the bonds of existence. By passion
the world is bound, by passion it is released.' †

At first glance it would seem that there were no restrictions at all . . . one could do as one liked—eat, drink,
indulge in sexual excesses, even commit murder and cannibalism, thereby finding salvation. Such practices were,
in fact carried out by 'fools'—(those who performed
Tantric rites without understanding or respect for their
inner meaning)—but for the man or woman who really
sought salvation, there was always the restraining influence of karma. The whole purpose of spiritual discipline was to attain a state where the cycle of rebirths
came to an end and the spirit was finally liberated, but

* *Kularnava Samhita.*
† Spoken by the Buddha in the *Hevajra Tantra.*

this could never be attained while fresh karma was being created by sins and wrong actions.

Karma also has another great significance in Tantric philosophy. If man is to reach ultimate freedom by working out or reaping the fruits of past incarnations the body must be kept alive, the race must go on. There must be food and there must be sexual intercourse and to ensure this God gave man desires for both, the strongest desires of the body. Eating and sexual intercourse are therefore divine acts, since they come from God. Only the ignorant, unaware of their divine origin, see them as impure animal actions. To the enlightened Tantric every woman personifies the Divine Mother, and sexual intercourse is a form of worship.* By this reasoning everyday life is raised to a higher spiritual level and is carried out in God's name. 'Eating and sexual union,' says the *Mahanirvana Tantra* (Tantra of the Great Liberation) 'are desired and natural to men, and their use is regulated for their benefit in the ordinance of Siva.'

So long as the motive is understood and action performed in the true spirit of devotion, enjoyment and liberation could exist side by side. Yoga, which liberates and *bhoga* (enjoyment) which creates further karma, could be reconciled, 'so long as such enjoyment be lawful and not sinful. *Bhoga* becomes complete yoga, bad deeds are made good deeds and the world becomes the seat of Liberation.'

The key to the paradox lies in the spiritual attitude of the practitioner.

TANTRIC TRAINING

The Tantra is non-sectarian. It provides paths of religious culture for all kinds of worshippers, recognizing three sorts of disciples. The lowest is the ordinary householder who must support a family and abide by social and other ties; next are those who, though still householders, have

---

* 'The fully wise *Sadhaka*, with honey, juice of sugar-cane, milk, corn, scents, garlands, dress and ornaments, should worship in union woman, who is the image of the Mother of the Universe. O Devi! the culture of the *Rasa* of sexual love consists in the worship of woman . . .'

freed themselves from most human passions, prejudices
and desires, living *in* but not *of* the world. The highest
are those saintly men who have given up home and family, all worldly ties and desires.

The disciple may follow a worldly or an ascetic path . . .
the Path of Desire *(Pravrtti)* or the Path of Cessation of
Desire *(Nivrtti)*. For a man who really seeks salvation
the first path could be used as a way to the second. Desires indulged without restraint, purely for self-gratifica-
tion, lead only to further desires, endlessly, till the Self
becomes completely submerged by the world. We all
know the people whose life is dedicated to acquiring possessions, increasingly obsessed with pleasure, and we all
know how aimless and dissatisfied they usually are. They
are engaged in a race that can never be won, that brings
only restlessness and discontent, for man is essentially a
spiritual being, and can never be really satisfied with
material toys. Thus the path of Desire animated only by
selfishness leads nowhere; but Desire regarded as a way
to liberation, animated by love of God could bring the
disciple to a true understanding of religious devotion
(bhakti) even if he never achieves complete liberation.

The process of graduating from the Path of Desire to
that of Renunciation may be slow. Accumulated *karma*
makes it difficult for all but the few to leap from the
abyss of *Pravrtti* to the celestial height of *Nivrtti* without
some preliminary training. In the *Principles of Tantra* we
are told:

'Spiritual self-culture . . . must be begun from the beginning. External worship leads to internal worship; internal worship purifies the mind; purity of mind induces
concentration and meditation; when meditation is ripe
communion *(Samadhi)* ensues and the *Sadhaka* (disciple) attains, at last, the highest Bliss.' *

For example, a man prays to his God to grant a
worldly desire, performing all necessary rites and ceremonies, austerities and penances. Though his original reason
for this devotion is selfish, he is, by these very observances, unconsciously developing his higher instincts. He
begins to value worship for its own sake. 'From hanker-

---

* *Tantratattva.*

ing after sensuous pleasure in the shape of money, power, fame, popularity, progeny . . . he gradually lifts his eyes upwards and longs for power in the unseen world. He devotes his mind and soul to its acquisition. And when he is fortunate enough to obtain but a morsel of it, he at once realizes the nothingness of worldly desires. He forthwith parts with them as a serpent parts with its dead skin.'

This is true voluntary renunciation, the only kind of any value. Once we have seen the genuine we are no longer interested in the imitation. Without a backward glance we gladly abandon the toys of this world for the realities of heaven. We are free.

The *Bhagavad Gita* says:

> 'The abstinent run away from what they desire
> But carry their desires with them.
> When a man enters Reality,
> He leaves his desires behind him.'

For most, however, the freedom of Renunciation is just out of reach; yet much can be gained on the path of Desire, if it is honestly followed. It is the path best suited to ordinary men and women, requiring them only to be devout, sincere, honest, kind and compassionate; to control greed and passions and to glorify God in their daily life.

'So long as a man is a householder, so long is his path the path of Desire *(Pravrtti)*. If he thinks that he has outgrown it, but at the same time earns money, enjoys the world, forms attachments and repulsions, seeks name, fame and popular applause, discharges the functions of a father of his household and a member of the community in which he lives, he deceives himself. The path pointed out to him by the Tantrik is the best that he can have as an individual, as the father of a family and as a member of society. The Tantrik culture is an all-round growth. It makes the body sturdy and strong, and proof to heat, cold and rain; it wards off diseases from without, and resists diseases from within; it makes one hardy, painstaking, and patient. His will being regularly trained, he is resolute and intrepid. All these qualities of body and mind render him as much a useful member of society as a humble supplicant for the dust of the Mother's feet.' *

An important feature of Tantric yoga—as of all yoga —is the spiritual guide or *guru*. Though the Tantric path could lead the disciple to heaven it could also lead him to hell if he lacks understanding. He is walking a tightrope of spiritual aspiration over a chasm of infernal flames and only the *guru* can save him from the false step that could destroy him. Tantric practices are essentially meant to be *experienced* by the disciple, yet the texts give little practical direction. They are for the most part fragmentary, cryptic, incoherent. Instructions for certain techniques are either inadequately described or entirely omitted. This is because knowledge was meant to be passed from mouth to ear, from *guru* to pupil. A step prematurely taken could set a man back many paces. Only the *guru* can decide if and when his disciple is spiritually ready for it.

For those on the path of Desire the *guru* should be a family man with wife and children . . . 'a householder, meditative and well-versed in Tantric knowledge . . . a man in, even if he be not of, the world.' An ascetic *guru* who is freed of the world, freed of *karma,* is unsuitable for those still enmeshed in worldly activities; but a householder-guru is in much the same situation as his disciple. Still remembering his own struggles, he can sympathise with difficulties and give understanding advice.

THE SECRET TEACHINGS. NOTORIETY OF THE TANTRAS

It is said 'Whereas the other scriptures are like a common woman, free to all, the Tantra is like a secret house-bride, to reveal which is death' . . . This secrecy has been the cause of a great deal of misinterpretation.

Not only are the texts frequently written in a secret ambiguous language intended to confuse non-initiates and 'fools' † but in many cases crude sexual and erotic terms and analogies are used to describe mystical states or spiritual experiences. This crudeness was a form of protest

---

* *Tantratattva.*
† See page 35.

against the growing over-intellectualization and compla-
cency of monastic life, an attempt to bring religious
thought once more into contact with ordinary earthly existence. The language was sometimes so obscene that
translators have been obliged to regard passages as un-
printable.

Through misunderstanding, unintentional or deliberate,
and through the liberal interpretation of symbolic acts,
orgies, drunkenness, sexual excesses, black magic, perversions, cannibalism and bloody sacrifice were carried on in
the name of Tantrism. Practices intended for detached in-
itiates and regarded as divine acts were deprived of their
spiritual meaning to become animal greed and lust; the
secrets of nature, of psychic power for attaining liberation
were perverted, used as black magic or exploited for
worldly ends. The misconceptions spread beyond India to
Europe and America where so-called Tantric Orders and
societies brought the name into further disrepute through
their excesses.

Yet it was not only the 'vulgar' who misunderstood the
teachings. Scholars, both Indian and European, were
equally guilty. Two examples of gross misinterpretation
are often quoted. The first is the verse, 'Having drunk,
drunk and again drunk, and having fallen, let him
rise again and attain liberation'. This, translated to read
that salvation comes through drinking to insensibility, refers to the rousing of Kundalini. The second, a passage
construed to mean that incest should be practised, is in
fact instructions for counting on the fingers during religious devotions.

Descriptions of Tantric rituals were little better. An account of the *Panchatattva* * published in 1822 is full of
righteous indignation:

'Many of the tuntrus . . . contain directions respecting
a most extraordinary and shocking mode of worship,
which is understood in a concealed manner among the
Hindus by the name of Chukru *(Cakra).* These Shastrus
direct, that the person who wishes to perform this ceremony must first in the night, choose a woman as the object of worship. If the person be a *dukshiracharee,* he

---

* Ritual of 5 Ms—worship with wine *(Madya)*, meat *(Mangsa)*, fish
(Matsya), grain (Mudra) and copulation . . . (Maithuna). See page 43.

must take his own wife; and if a *Vamacharee,* the daugh-
ter of a dancer, a *kupalee,* a washerwoman, a barber, a
chundalu, or of a Musulman, or a prostitute; and place
her on a seat, or mat; and then bring broiled fish, flesh,
fried peas, rice, spirituous liquors, sweetmeats, flowers
and other offerings, which as well as the female must be
purified by the repeating of incantations. To this succeeds
the worship of the guardian deity; and after this, that of
the female, who sits naked . . .' (Here the author breaks
into asterisks) . . .

'Here things too abominable to enter the ears of man,
and impossible to be revealed to a Christian public, are
contained in the directions of the shastrus.

'The learned bramhum who opened to me these abominations made several efforts—paused and began again—
and then paused again—before he could mention the
shocking indecencies presented by his own shastrus.'

'. . . She (the woman) partakes of the offerings, even
of the spirituous liquors; and of the flesh though it should
be that of the cow . . . the spirituous liquors must be
drank by measure; and the company while eating must
put food into each other's mouths. The priest then—in
the presence of all—behaves towards this female in a
manner which decency forbids to be mentioned; after
which the persons present repeat many times the name of
some god, performing actions unutterably abominable
and here, this most diabolical business closes.

'At present the persons committing these abominations
(Vamacharees) are becoming more and more numerous
and in proportion as they increase, the ceremonies are
more and more indecent . . . Those who abide by the
rules of the Shastrus are comparatively few; the generality
confine themselves chiefly to those parts that belong to
gluttony, drunkenness and whoredom.' *

Though later accounts show that the writers were
aware of the significance behind the ritual they are still
filled with such phrases as 'scandalous orgies' . . . 'gross
indecencies' . . . 'a licentious worship that leads to
cruelty, self-indulgence and sensual gratification . . .

'On occasion of worship the female votaries are said

---

* Ward, W. *A view of the History, Literature and Mythology of the
Hindus.* 1822.

to deposit their upper vests in a box in charge of the
guru. At the close of the usual rites the male worshippers
take each a vest from the box and the female to whom
the garment appertains, be she ever so nearly of kin to
him, is the partner for the time of his licentious
pleasure.' *

There are, of course, reasons for these misunderstand-
ings and confusions. The Tantras *were* abused, *were* regarded by 'fools' as authority for unlimited licence; and
even when this was not so, the texts were so obscure, so
long inaccessible that non-initiates could hardly be
blamed for failing to understand or see the spiritual significance behind the 'scandalous' acts. It was not until Sir
John Woodroffe began the collection, translation and
publication of his Tantric Texts in 1912 that a clearer
picture of Tantrism started to emerge.

It must be remembered that the earliest English accounts were written at the worst period of our puritanical
prudery; also at a time when white men believed themselves superior to coloured races and held that the lowest
of their own cultural or religious practices were infinitely
better than the highest of Indian philosophy.

Men of such mentality were unlikely to sympathize
with Tantrism or appreciate its aims. They remained ignorant of the great and compassionate teaching that all
men and women have within them the hidden capacity
for enlightenment; that the Tantras are the guide for spiritual training by which the obscuring cloud of ignorance
may be lifted.

INTERCOURSE AS A RITUAL

'When sexual love realizes the Supreme Object, then is
Supreme Tranquillity.'

Ritual intercourse was practised in India, as in other
ancient civilizations, from very early times, often as a fer-
tility rite; but in Tantrism it was regarded as part of spiritual training, as a means of attaining Supreme Bliss.

It is often claimed that the *Panchatattva*, which in-

---

* Wilson, H. H. *Essays and lectures on the Religion of the Hindus.*

cluded ritual copulation, was purely symbolic, that it referred only to the uniting forces within the yogi's own
body;* but though it could be thus interpreted, it was also
carried out in the literal sense. It was not, however, a
drunken orgy. It was intended to be performed without
thirst or lust, with longing for the satisfaction of the *De-
vata* alone. Before a disciple could participate he must
learn its inner meaning from his *guru,* otherwise he became a sinner; but 'he who partakes of the five articles,
knowing from the mouth of the *guru* their true significance, is liberated.'

To the Tantric every woman personified the Divine
Mother. In the *Panchatattva* the naked woman worshipped . . . 'richly ornamented, sprinkled with wine,
sanctified by mantra . . .' was no longer regarded as ordinary flesh and blood but as a goddess, as *Sakti,* as
cosmic energy, or as Supreme Wisdom. Intercourse between her and the yogi symbolised integration, Supreme
Bliss, Perfection of Wisdom. If the woman was not so regarded, her body not recognized as a mystical symbol of
universal creation, and the rite practised without detachment, reverence and belief in its inner meaning, it was no
more than ordinary intercourse, even a sin, which created
fresh karma to bind the 'fool'.

To assist the transformation of physical copulation to a
sacred ritual, of the yogi and his partner into divine
beings, certain preliminaries were observed. The woman,
'young, beautiful and learned' must be trained and in-
structed by a *guru,* her body purified and consecrated.
The yogi, who must be in the highest state of physical
training, underwent intense purification followed by meditation and certain preliminary ceremonies and observances. He must train himself to regard the yogini as a divine being. Intercourse must be practiced according to the
traditional rites if it were to bring liberation and not fall
into the chain of karma.

---

* 'In the higher yogic practice these become drinking of the wine
which flows from the centre of the 1000-petalled lotus at the summit
of the head; killing lust, anger, greed, delusions and other evil beasts;
cooking the fish of deceit, calumny, envy, etc.; showing the gestures of
hope, desire and contempt, and enjoying the lustful beauties along the
spinal cord. The 5 actions lead man to inner perfection.'—*Hevajra Tantra*
trs. by D. L. Snellgrove (Oxford University Press).

The sexual union of yogi and yogini* symbolised non-duality, reintegration, reunion of the two principles; but intercourse must not end in ejaculation of semen. As the celibate yogi conserves seminal energy through suppression or transmutation, the Tantric also conserves it, 'even in the embrace of a woman' by hatha-yoga techniques. He who can simultaneously arrest breath, thought and semen achieves the unity, supreme bliss he seeks through *maithuna.* But the seed must not fall . . . 'the falling of seed leads towards death, the keeping of one's seed is life.' Not only does loss of seed bring old age and death but it turns the divine symbolic union to ordinary sexual intercourse.

If the seed does fall, it must be drawn back into the yogi's body, and at the same time he must take in the yogini's sexual fluid or 'female seed'. Male and female will then be united within the yogi and duality abolished. For this purpose, intercourse is continued until the female essence is emitted and the male on the point of ejaculation. The skilled adept then holds back the *bindu,* while drawing in his partner's genital secretion.

Even when texts are available, the non-initiate finds little enlightenment on these practices. In the *Hevajra,* a famous Buddhist Tantra, there are no directions for this physical control in the Ritual of Union. Instructions are often ambiguous and confusing, for the ritual could be interpreted either literally or symbolically.

When intercourse between male and female is practised according to this Tantra the yogi personifies Means, the yogini Wisdom. In their union there is 'neither passion nor absence of passion nor yet a middle state. Because of its freedom from all three the Innate is called Perfect Enlightenment'.

The performance is preceded by preparation, purification, meditation. 'Meditation is good if performed at night

* Even here, sexual intercourse could be symbolic, referring to processes within the yogi's own body:

'The two lips of the worshippers are the two casual principles, Siva and his power Sakti; the movement of the lips is their coition (*maithuna*), the sound which springs forth from them . . . is the point-limit (*bindu*), the sperm, the point from which manifestation arises; the deity engendered is thus in a way a creation, a son of the worshipper.'—Sir John Woodroffe: *A Garland of Letters.*

beneath a lonely tree or in a cemetery, or in the mother's house, or in some unfrequented spot.

'When some heat has been developed, if one wishes to perform this practice and gain perfection, then upon this course one should proceed.

'Take a girl of the *vajra*-family, fair-featured and large-eyed and endowed with youth and beauty; who has been consecrated by oneself and is possessed of a compassionate disposition, and with her the practice should be performed . . . Take her then who is now consecrated with the depositing of the seed of enlightenment.

'Taking this girl, who has wide-open eyes and is of age and endowed with youth and beauty, he should consecrate her with the seed of enlightenment. Beginning with the ten rules of virtuous conduct, he should expound to her the *Dharma,* how the mind is fixed on the divine form, on the meaning of symbolic forms and concerning one-pointedness of mind, and in one month she will be fit, of that there is no doubt. And so the girl is there, now freed from all false notions, and received as though she were a boon. Or else he should produce a *Mudra* (girl) by conjuring her forth by his own power from amongst the gods or titans or men . . . Then taking her, one should perform the practice, with the realization of one's own composure. For this practice, which is called terrifying in appearance, is not taught for the sake of enjoyment but for the examination of one's own thought, whether the mind is steady or waving.'

The yogini is not to be touched for enjoyment, nor even regarded as a woman. 'Relinquishing her form as a woman, she would assume that of her lord. Gone are her breasts, and his *vajra* * is manifest with a bell on each side, where the *lotus* * had been.

'I.x Consecration.

'(a) (2) First the yogi, himself the essence of the God, should purify the site and having zealously prepared the requisite protection, he should then inscribe the *mandala.* In a garden or in a lonely spot or in a *bodhisattva's* house . . . one should lay out the *mandala* . . . The celestial spell who comes of the Five Families should be placed

---

* 1. *Vajra* and 2. *lotus*—male and female sex organs.

46 *Sex and Yoga*

there (6) or whatsoever sixteen-year-old girl is found. A
yogini is resorted to, so long as she possesses *sukra*
(semen, energy) (7) One binds the face of the *Projna*
(yogini) and likewise of the *Upaya* (yogi) and the prod-
uct of the service rendered one drops into the pupil's
mouth (8). In that very act the flavour of sameness
should be placed within the pupil's range. (b) From self-
experiencing comes this knowledge, which is free from
ideas of self and other (9) like the sky it is pure and
void, the essence supreme of non-existence and existence,
a mingling of Wisdom and Means, a mingling of passion
and absence of passion. (10) It is the life of living things,
it is the Unchanging One Supreme; it is all-pervading,
abiding in alll embodied things (11) It is the stuff the
world is made of, and in it existence and non-existence
have their origin . . .' *

Ritual intercourse is in four stages:

> 'First is just Joy
> Secondly is Joy Supreme,
> Thirdly, is the Joy of Cessation
> Fourth is the Joy Innate.' †

'The first Joy is of this world, the second Joy is of this
world, the third Joy is of this world, but the Innate exists
not in these three.'

The four Joys are also distinguished by four Moments:
Variety, Development, Consummation and Blank.

'It is called *Variety,* because it involves different things,
the embrace, the kiss and so forth. *Development* is the
reverse of this, for it is the experiencing of blissful knowledge. *Consummation* is defined as the reflection that this
bliss has been experienced by oneself. *Blank* is quite
other than these three, and knows neither passion nor absence of passion. The first Joy is found in Variety, Perfect
Joy in Development, the Joy of Cessation in Consummation and the Joy of the Innate in Blank.‡

---

*These, and following quotations are taken from *The Hevajra Tantra*: a
critical study by D. L. Snellgrove. London. Oxford University Press. 1959.
† 'The first comes by desire for contact' (of *vajra* and *lotus*) 'the second by
desire for bliss, the third from the passing of passion and by this means the
fourth is realized.'
‡ In the physical sense, this refers to the practice of provoking, then arresting the seminal flow.

'These four Joys are to be experienced in due order in accordance with the list of the four consecrations . . . The first is represented by a smile, the second by a gaze, the third in an embrace, and the fourth in union. This fourfold set of consecrations is for the purpose of perfecting living-beings. The word consecration or sprinkling is used because one is sprinkled or cleansed.

'The *Prajna* of sixteen years he clasps within his arms and from the union of the *vajra* and bell the Master's consecration comes about. She is fair-featured, wide-eyed and endowed with youth and beauty. Then with thumb and fourth finger he drops the *bindu* in the pupil's mouth. In that very act the flavour of sameness should be placed within the pupil's range. Then having honoured and worshipped the *Prajna,* he should consign her to the pupil, saying 'Oh Great Being, take thou the *Mudra* who will bring you bliss', and knowing his pupil to be worthy, free of envy and wrath, he then further commands him: 'Be ye one, O Vajradhrk.'

'Now I shall tell you of the pupil's part and how he begs for consecration, how he pronounces words of praise and worship when he beholds his master with the *Mudra* (yogini).

'Oh great tranquil Lord, intent on the *vajra*-practice,
Thou perfector of the Symbol, that has thine origin in
the oneness of the indestructible *vajra,*
As you now do for yourself, may you also do for me.
I am sunk in the thick mud of the *samsara.*
Save me who am without a helper.'

'Then with pleasing food and drink, with wine and meat of good quality, with incense, oblations, and garlands, with bells and banners and ointments, with all these he should honour his lord.

'When the pupil has now reached the moment of Perfect Joy which is free from all notions of diversity, the master should say: "Oh Great Being, hold thou to the great bliss. Until the time of enlightenment, O Vajrahrk, serve thou the cause of beings." Thus should speak the Adamantine Lord as he sees his pupil overwhelmed in compassion.'

Intercourse also symbolizes the five elements: earth, water, fire, air, space.

'From the contact that comes of the union of *vajra* and *lotus,* there arises the effect of hardness . . . The *bodhi-citta* (semen) is a flow and this flow is deemed as water . . . From the rubbing together of two things fire always arises . . . The *bodhicitta* in the *lotus* has the nature of air . . . The blood is bliss and passion and the nature of bliss is space . . .

'At the union of *vajra* and *lotus,* earth arises there from that contact with the quality of hardness. From the flow of *sukra* (semen) water rises, and fire from the friction. Wind comes from the motion, and space corresponds to the bliss . . .'

After the act of *maithuna* the disciple is considered free to devote himself to meditation and physical discipline. If he gains mastery of himself he may wear the five symbolic ornaments and may join other perfected yogis and yoginis on the eighth or fifteenth day of the dark fortnight, to drink wine, eat meat, dance, sing and experience the Supreme Bliss.

Perfected yogis and yoginis recognize each other by secret signs and by similar signs show whether or not they wish to practise *maithuna.*

YOGIC-SEXUAL TECHNIQUES USED IN TANTRISM

In many instances Tantric and Hatha-yoga practices overlap. Methods of suspending breath, thought and semen, and of absorbing the female essence for the purpose of achieving liberation are hatha-yoga techniques.

The four Joys or Moments mentioned in the Hevajra *Tantra,* when experienced through coitus, correspond to the process of provoking the *bindu* or semen to the stage of ejaculation, then arresting it while breath and thought are suspended.

In the yoga texts, as in the Tantras, descriptions of these physical practices are usually incomplete and mingled with esoteric terms and references to psychic processes. They are essentially intended to be taught by a *guru,* from mouth to ear, to be learnt by practical experi-

ence. For example, *Vajroli mudra,* by which male and female seed are absorbed, is described thus, by the god
Siva, in the *Siva Samhita:*

'First the wise seeker should try to draw in, through
the channel of the sex organ, the female seed from the
yoni and bring it into his own body, and he should move
his sex organ without letting his own seed fall. If by
chance the seed begins to move, then, through the *yoni-
mudra* it should be stopped and drawn upward and stored
on the left side, then stopping for a moment the movement of the *lingam* and following the instructions given
by his *guru,* the yogi, uttering repeatedly the syllables
"Hun", should again move his *linga* in the *yoni.* And forcibly drawing inward the *Apana* air he should draw in the
seed of the woman, this is known as *Varjroli mudra.*'

'If I who am the male seed and Shakti who is the female seed are united, then, when performing this practice,
the yogi gains a divine body (i.e. his body becomes like
that of the gods).'

'The falling of seed leads towards death, the keeping of
one's seed is life. Hence with all his power should a man
hold his seed.'

'In this world all is born from seed and dies of seed.
Knowing this the yogi should always keep his seed.'

'By this practice even the man who indulges in worldly
pleasures can attain realization, and all wished-for results
can in this world be achieved.'

'There are two varieties of *Vajroli* named *Sahajoli* and
Amaroli. The yogi should in any case try to avoid loosing
his seed.'

'If by chance the sperm should suddenly fall and the
union of moon and sun (male and female seed) take
place, this is known as *Amaroli.* The united seeds should
then be drawn up again through the *linga.*'

'When his seed begins to move, but the yogi is able
through the *yoni* gesture to stop it, this is known as *Sahajoli* and is a most secret process in all the scriptures of
earthly wisdom.'

The *yoni gesture* is also described in *Siva Samhita: Yoni
gesture (yoni-mudra)* is the contraction of the *yoni* place
behind the male organ.

'First with the help of in-breathing (*Puraka*) draw in

the mind with the breath to the basic Centre (*Adhara*)
(and maintain it there firmly). Then try to contract the
yoni place between the male organ and the anus.

'Then concentrate on Lust (*Kama*), which, in the
shape of an arrow shining like a thousand suns but cool
like a thousand moons, lies in the centre of the principal
yoni. Above it is a subtle tongue of light which is Consciousness, the Supreme Energy (*Kala*), and in union
with it is the one Supreme Self on whom one should med-
itate.'

'*Yoni-mudra* is practised in the Adept posture with one
heel pressed against the anus and the other concealing the
male organ. Ears, eyes, nose and mouth are also sealed
by the Ten-finger gesture. Through this exercise, it is
said, Kundalini awakens and rises through the central ar-
tery (*sushumna*) of the subtle body and successively
reaches the three emblems (*lingas*) (corresponding to the
gross, subtle and causal shape). And in the heavenly,
(the higher) region he drinks the divine ambrosia which
is Supreme Bliss, white and red in colour, shining like a
thousand suns, and cool as a thousand moons, which
flows like a rain of nectar. And he then returns to the
yoni.'

Modern investigators have suggested that the arrest of
semen and its return is achieved by extraordinary mastery
over non-striated muscles which normally cannot be controlled. This is no more remarkable than the fully-trained
adept's ability to suspend breath or heart-beat or to control nerves and circulation.

In the *Siva Samhita* it is said that control over the
bindu is attained through practise while urinating. Air is
drawn up through the urethra and very little water
passed. This must be done under the guidance of a *guru*,
takes a very long time to perfect and few ever master it.
Those who do, it is said, have complete control of *bindu*,
even in sleep. They are also believed to emanate tranquillity and a sweet scent like the lotus blossom.

The process as described in the *Hathayogapradipika* is
little more explicit:

'Two things are necessary for this . . . milk, and a
woman behaving as desired. By practising to draw in the
bindu discharged during cohabitation, whether one be a

man or a woman, one obtains success in the practice of
Vajroli. By means of a pipe, one should blow air slowly
into the passage in the male organ. By practice the discharged *bindu* is drawn up. One can draw back and preserve one's own discharged *bindu.* The yogi who can protect his *bindu* thus, overcomes death; because death
comes by discharging *bindu,* and life is prolonged by its
preservation. By preserving *bindu,* the body of the yogi
emits a pleasing smell. There is no fear of death, so long
as the *bindu* is well established in the body. Hence, mind
and *bindu* should be protected by all means.'

Even a man who lives a worldly life and does not follow the rules of yoga 'deserves success and is a yogi' if he
performs *Vajroli.*

It should not be necessary to emphasize again the dangers of attempting these methods without the constant su-
pervision of a highly trained teacher, but there are always
some who ignore the warnings. The present authors recently received a plea for help and advice from a man
who had tried to learn *Vajroli-mudra* from a brief extract
quoted in a book. In the process he had damaged bladder, nervous system and general health.

These techniques were also practised by the yogis of
the Nath cult, mentioned on page 15, many of whose
teachings were very similar to Hatha yoga . . . developing and cultivating the body to perfection; delaying
change, old age and death; attainment of immortality
through bodily perfection . . . Though ascetics, and re-
garding women as man's chief destroyer, they practised
the sexual-yogic techniques of *Vajroli, Amaroli* and *Sa-
haroli;* but the women used as partners were regarded
purely as a means to an end, without any of the deifica-
tion or idealization of the Tantrics.

LATER TANTRIC CULTS

A number of cults developed out of Tantrism. Some were
degenerate; black magic, cannibalism, sexual orgies, etc.,
were practiced without thought of spiritual attainment;
others were animated by a true desire for liberation.
Amongst these last were the *Buddhist* and *Vaisnava Sahajaya Cults,* both intimately involved with yoga practice.

As with other esoteric movements, these cults were based on the belief that man can never free himself from his sexual instincts no matter how long he struggles or how hard he tries repression and discipline; that it is better to accept the instinct as a fundamental part of his nature, to use it as a means of spiritual development and self-realization. Since even the grossest form of sexual pleasure brings some kind of liberation, discipline of mind and body, could raise this natural impulse to a higher level by purging it of all grossness, transforming it to a spiritual experience.

The Buddhist *Sahajayist* cult—which developed from Tantric Buddhism—believed that the most intense sex emotion produced under perfect yoga control could bring about the emptiness of mind and suspension of thought necessary for experiencing Supreme Bliss. In this mindless state duality is lost. There is no more subject-object but full realization and a return to the primal non-duality.

As in Hatha yoga, the *Sahajayists* believed the body must be perfected and strengthened to stand training and discipline, and that retention of semen was of vital importance in increasing mental and physical health and power.

Sexo-yogic practices used to unite seed and ovum brought Supreme Bliss.

Supreme Bliss was held to have two aspects . . . first, gross sexual pleasure ending in discharge of semen; second, the motionless aspect of bliss through arrest of the *bindu*. Through yoga training and methods the *Sahajayist* achieved the first aspect of intercourse; then by arrest, transformed it to the second, turning physical pleasure achieved with a partner to the subtle inexpressible joy of liberation.

The secret practice of transforming sex-pleasure to Supreme Bliss by yoga methods was a most important part of *Sahajaya* training. During intercourse the yogi was identified as *Prajna* (Wisdom) or as Siva; the woman as *Upaya* (Means) or as *Sakti*. Their union brought non-duality.

The *Vaisnava Sahajayists* identified all men with Krishna (the Enjoyer) and all women with Radha (the

Enjoyed).* Physical love between man and woman was a gross manifestation of the pure love between Krishna and Radha.

To achieve *Sahaja* there must be a mystical transformation. Both man and woman must first realize their true selves as Krishna and Radha, must through long training and discipline learn to transform themselves into divine figures, completely free of animal instincts. An important part of this training was a process known as *Aropa* (attribution of divinity to man) by which their love became divine, transcending gross sensuality.

Without this divine transformation there was only a carnal act which could send the practitioners to hell.

Like Tantrism, this cult could hardly escape abuse or the reputation of being 'an order of debauchery under the cloak of religion'; yet its essential principle, based on understanding of man's fallibility as much as his aspirations, was that divine love does not demand rejection of human love. Human life, human love, the human body were considered as important and real as the spirit. Human beauty inspires human passion, which, by appropriate training and discipline could bring understanding of divine love; love and worship of the human body leads to Supreme Bliss. Man only finds full realization of his own nature through the woman he loves; through their physical union they experience pure love between their inner selves as Krishna and Radha.

The *Vaisnava Sahajayists* recognized three kinds of women disciples—those with no selfish wish for satisfaction, who desired only their lover's happiness; those who expected an equal share of enjoyment; and those who wanted only self-satisfaction. The first were the highest, personifying Radha's pure and selfless love for Krishna. Only they were considered suitable for the culture of love.

Male disciples were classified as Beginners, Advanced and Perfected. Only the Advanced could practice with a

---

* Man and woman were also believed to represent the 2 flows of love known as *Rasa*—the ultimate emotion as enjoyer, and *Rati*—the object of *Rasa*, or the enjoyed. Also as *Kama*, the lover that attracts, and *Madana*, the exciting cause of his love. Their union produced *Sahaja*, the emotion of purest love.

woman; only the Perfected could fully experience real
love.

The practice of love was governed by strict conditions.
The disciple underwent severe physical and mental discipline. The body must be perfected, strengthened and purified, the mind completely purged of all base instincts so
the divine nature was released. There must be full mastery of the secret yogic-sexual practices of controlling the
bindu.

During the course of training and the culture of love
the yogi not only freed himself of his animal nature but
gradually came to see the woman as a goddess. For some
time he waited on her hand and foot and slept at her feet.
Then, while still acting as her Servant, he slept on her left
side; at a later stage on her right side; then in her arms
. . . gradually learning thus to control his senses in her
presence. The final act of union was preceded by intense
concentration and meditation, for he must learn not to
touch her 'for the sake of bodily pleasure but for the perfecting of the spirit'.

Ceremonial intercourse (*maithuna*) comprises eight
parts, 'beginning with *sadhana,* mystical concentration
with the help of liturgical formulas; then follows *smarana,*
("recollections", "penetration into consciousness'); *aropa*
("attribution of qualities to the object") in which flowers
are ceremonially offered to the *nayika* (who is beginning
to be transformed into a goddess); *manana* ("remembering the woman's beauty when she is absent"), which is
already an interiorization of the ritual. In the fifth stage,
dhyana ("mystical meditation") the woman sits on the
yogi's left and is embraced "in such wise that the spirit
is inspired". In the *puja* (the "cult", properly speaking),
the place where the *nayika* is seated receives worship,
offerings are made, and the *nayika* is bathed as if she
were the statue of a goddess. During this time the yogi
mentally repeats formulas. His concentration reaches its
maximum when he carries the *nayika* in his arms and lays
her on the bed, repeating the formula: *Hling kling kan-
darpa svaha.* The union that takes place is between two
"gods". The erotic play is realized on a transphysiological

plane, for it never comes to an end. During the *maithuna,* the yogi and his *nayika* embody a "divine condition" in the sense that they not only experience bliss but are also able to contemplate the ultimate reality directly.' *

---

* Eliade, Mircea: *Yoga, Immortality and Freedom.*

4

The Path of the Householder

Karma yoga, Hatha yoga and Bhakti yoga. The Jaina
yogis. Rules and practices. Restraints and observances.

Ascetic restrictions, Tantric rituals are not for the average
man. His is the 'mixed' way—a little of the Vedic, a little
of the Tantric; the way of moderation.

There is no formal path for the householder among the
classical schools; yet this does not prevent him practising
yoga in the true sense of the word. As we know, a yogi is
essentially one who seeks yoga or union of the individual
spirit with the Universal Spirit by means that harm no
one.

In most cases a householder yogi works out his own
path, drawing on different yogas. Basically a Karma yogi
(one who lives by right action), he could also practice
Bhakti, the yoga of love and devotion, while observing
the *yamas* and *niyamas* (restraints and observances) of
Hatha yoga, as well as many of its physical disciplines
and breathing exercises.

None of these practices need take him away from
home and family life or his responsibilities to society.
Any withdrawing is done inwardly, as a change of heart.
It involves no loss of kindness or affection for others or
indifference to their sufferings; on the contrary, it brings
the all-embracing compassion and tolerance that comes
from a sense of true values.

KARMA YOGA

In the *Bhagavad-Gita,* the meaning of this yoga is explained by the god Krishna:

'. . . In this world, aspirants may find enlightenment
by two different paths. For the contemplative is the path
of knowledge; for the active is the path of selfless action.'
. . . 'You have the right to work, but for the work's sake
only.' . . . 'Desire for the fruits must never be your motive in working' . . . 'Perform every action with your
heart fixed on the Supreme Lord.' . . . 'Be even-tem-
pered in success and failure, for it is this evenness of tem-
per which is meant by yoga.' . . . 'Work done with anxiety about results is far inferior to work done without such
anxiety, in the calm of self-surrender' . . . 'They who
work selfishly for results are miserable;' '. . . when a
man has found delight and satisfaction and peace in the
Atman * then he is no longer obliged to perform any
kind of action. He has nothing to gain in this world by
action, and nothing to lose by refraining from action. He
is independent of everybody and everything. Do your
duty always, but without attachment. That is how a man
reaches the ultimate Truth; by working without anxiety
about results.'

> 'The ignorant work
> For the fruit of their actions:
> The wise must work also
> Without desire.
> Pointing man's feet
> To the path of his duty.
> Let the wise beware
> Lest they bewilder
> The minds of the ignorant
> Hungry for action:
> Let them show by example
> How work is holy
> When the heart of the worker
> Is fixed on the Highest.' †

* Self-realization.

† *Bhagavad-Gita.* trs. by Prabhavananda *and* Isherwood.

To work honestly, without enslavement to greed, competition, vanity; to enjoy the fruits of work without attachment or possessiveness; to remember that important as they seem to us now, our pleasures and work are after all only toys which in the end we must leave behind, does not mean a joyless existence or a negative attitude; it is simply seeing life in perspective. Eventually, the Karma yogi who attains Self-realization, finds the truth of all this. In a sense, his work is then finished though he goes on with it till his death; but even those who never reach this stage are not lost. 'Even if a man falls away from the practice of yoga, he will still win the heaven of the doers of good deeds, and dwell there many years,' . . . 'No one who seeks *Brahman* (God) ever comes to an evil end.'

HATHA YOGA

This is the path of bodily strength and control and the practices and *asanas* in this book form part of its physical teachings. We know that hatha yoga is not merely a matter of physical culture. It is a form of training to strengthen and equip the disciple for the highest stages of breath control and meditation, with the ultimate objective of stilling body and mind in the state of *samadhi;* but the benefits of this preliminary training are available to all who are not debarred by physical disability.

The *yamas* and *niyamas* (restraints and observances) provide a system of character training for developing moral strength. They are the basis of all good and honourable conduct. The restraints are concerned with violence or causing pain, lying, stealing, chastity and possession; the observances with purity, (mental and physical), contentment (philosophical acceptance), austerity (physical and mental discipline) and devotion to God.

Though the detached disciple must observe the *yamas* and *niyamas* to the letter, the householder could follow some of them in a more general way. To the ascetic yogi chastity means complete celibacy, but the householder could interpret it as avoidance of unlawful lust, marital infidelity, licentious thoughts and words; nor need he take physical purification or austerities to the lengths of the real hatha yogi.

BHAKTI YOGA

The *Yoga SaraSangraha* includes knowledge, love and action as methods of yoga. This could be interpreted as the paths of Jnani yoga, Bhakti yoga and Karma yoga, or more simply in the everyday sense of understanding, loving-kindness and honourable constructive deeds.

Though the path of Jnani yoga, in its higher sense, is too difficult and demanding for the ordinary householder, Bhakti is within the capacity of all. It includes not only love and devotion to God but love for all things, all people. It is the simplest yet most profound of all ways, for love in any form is the greatest, most constructive force in the world. Love automatically creates understanding, patience, kindness, tolerance, generosity, loyalty, goodwill and peace. If the world were ruled by love there would be no war, no fear and distrust. It is the basis of all great spiritual teachings and philosophies and it demands no arduous training or disciplines for it is a natural instinct in man. It requires only the faith to go on loving, if need be in the face of ingratitude, indifference, even hostility.

Though Bhakti is sometimes belittled by the arrogant as unintellectual, and has been criticised as leading to religious fanaticism, it should be present in all yoga. It is the most suitable path for the common man and is the most popular among the Indian people. In Tantrism it is recognized as a necessary preliminary to the higher Jnani yoga, even as a means of achieving *samadhi*. ('The important work of awakening the Divine Serpent (*Kundalini*) is as much within the reach of the Tantric Bhakti yogi as it is of the Jnani yogi.') The state of ecstasy experienced through religious adoration and contemplation is as common in the West as the East.

As for the rest of us . . . 'As householders we are chained to the world by a thousand and one knots. Our family, our lust, our greed, our avarice, our ambition, all bind us down . . . altruism is, in many a case, traceable to love of fame, love of popular applause, love of power, and other little self-loves. It is intense love of God alone which can make a person selfless in action . . .' just as it is selfless action that leads to knowledge of God.

This is the way of the Householder, living in but not of the world. He recognizes the true nature of the Spirit but respects the body as its temple. He may practice hatha yoga to keep healthy, in good spirits, maintain vital energy and sexual potency, to help achieve serenity and inner strength. Trying to follow the yogic restraints and observances to the best of his ability, he leads a good, useful and satisfying life; and though he may never know the full ecstasy of the dedicated ascetic, he may experience moments when he is so at one, so in tune with the universe that he feels only love for all creation.

SEX AND THE HOUSEHOLDER

The two strongest primitive impulses in man are hunger and sex. By the laws of nature he demands food for survival and sex (reproduction) for the continuance of the species. Satisfaction of these natural impulses is necessary to his mental and bodily health and deprivation of either usually ends in physical or psychological disorders.

The importance of correct nutrition is now fully appreciated but in matters of sex we still swing from intense interest to ignorance, from excessive frankness to puritanical prudery, from down-to-earth commonsense to hypocritical evasion. This, no doubt, will continue until proper education on the subject is available to all. Unlike the hunger for food, sex in civilized man is a complex need, varying with individuals in it psycho-physical requirements.

In many Christian countries it is still secretly associated with sin and shame. Pure spiritual love is exalted but physical love is considered animal. The Tantras, on the contrary, recognizing its importance, taught that intercourse between men and women was a divine act, and sin, shame, bestial and animal aspects were seen in it only by those whose minds harboured such thoughts.

In the ascetic Jaina communities, spread throughout

India, family life is only permitted 'in deference to human frailty', and as preparation for a fully ascetic existence. The rules are stringent. The householder may have intercourse with his own wife only when he cannot withstand his sexual impulse or when he has found lust cannot be destroyed by meditation. There are many taboos for non-celibate laymen, such as intercourse with a mistress or a temporary wife; with an unmarried (unprotected) woman; exciting sexual passions by artificial stimuli, excessive love-play or deviations; over-indulgence in sensual pleasure, including taking aphrodisiacs. For a woman, the offenses include taking a lover; trying to seduce her husband when he is under a vow of celibacy, or, when there is more than one wife, stealing a co-wife's night with the husband.

Eighteen kinds of abstinence are defined, among them the sight of women's bodies . . . staring at or touching any female organ, human or animal; imagining or speaking of intercourse. An emission of semen in sleep must be followed by recitation of prayers and meditation upon the sacred doctrine.

Copulation is divided into two types . . . animate and inanimate. The first includes copulation of a man with any female, celestial, human or animal; with another man; with a hermaphrodite; with himself (masturbation); and, for women, masturbation, or using the root of a plant as artificial phallus. For men, inanimate copulation could be with a female painting or statue; with the current of a river; with clay; and for women, with a wooden phallus or similar apparatus.

The Jaina yogis compare sexual relations with women to a fever that brings delirium and exhausts the body. Not only does it destroy the tranquillity of the soul but it can never give true satisfaction, since desire can only breed more desire.

One of the Jainist sects believes that women can never achieve liberation in this life, being full of impurity. They harbour thousands of living creatures in their armpits, navel and sexual parts. Each time intercourse takes place hundreds of these tiny lives are destroyed.

Perhaps the wisest and most reasonable attitude is found in the *Kama Sutra,* the ancient Indian treatise on the art of love. The author, Vatsyayana, writing many hundreds of years ago, advises that the best life for a man is religious study in youth, working for material comforts and practising the art of love in his middle years; and an old age devoted to religious exercises and observances, leading to liberation. He believes that the pleasures of love are as necessary as food but should not be indulged to excess, and that the art of love must be learnt if it is to bring happiness and become more than an animal act.

This could well be the pattern for the Householder's sex life. Healthy, vital, free of sin and shame, avoiding excesses of indulgence or of abstinence, he could regard sex as a form of worship to God, believing that 'Divinity . . . dwells as light in the stars, in sperm as the power of generation, and in sex as pleasure.' *

---

* *Taittiryia Upanishad.*

5

Yoga and the Reproductive System

Male and female systems; Puberty; menstruation; menopause; sexual ageing; Importance of endocrinal glands. Yoga's role in maintaining health and potency. Disorders of the reproductive system benefiting from yoga.

In the lowest forms of life, reproduction does not involve sexual intercourse—the physical union of male and female. Bacteria, amoeba, certain worms, etc., reproduce by binary fission, either splitting into parent and offspring or by the absorption, as it were, of the parent cell into the new life.

In more highly evolved creatures the process is more complicated, requires a more complex reproductive system. At one end of the scale is the unicellular organism, entirely contained in its one cell; at the other, the delicate, intricate, subtle, mysterious human reproductive system.

Though man's generative organs may no longer present any great mystery to modern medical science (though even here much is still not understood), the psychological and emotional aspects of human mating remain very much an unknown. These forces, which help distinguish man from the animals, have the power to raise him to a life of happiness or cast him into misery.

Such vulnerability is one of the prices we pay for our higher state of evolution. Psychological disturbances, inhibitions, complexes, deviations, emotional problems of all kinds help complicate human sex life; while the intricate nature of the reproductive system itself, particularly in women, the delicacy of the glandular balance with its powerful influence on mind and body, lay us open to all sorts of physical disorders.

Though many of these mental and emotional disturbances are beyond the scope of this book, as are many physical conditions, yoga practice could contribute to maintaining equilibrium and the health of the reproductive system. Much mental unhappiness and physical suffering might be avoided by simple measures taken in time or by a little knowledge and experience.

Not only is the sex mechanism with its complex system of nerves and muscles extremely delicate in itself, but it is greatly influenced by the condition of the endocrinal glands, supplies of vital energy, general nervous, organic and muscular health.

Sexual desire (*libido*) is created in the brain by impressions received there through the senses . . . sight, touch, etc. Impulses are then sent out from the brain to the sex centre in the lower part of the spine and thence to the nerves controlling the sex organs. Body and mind are so closely interrelated in sex that weaknesses or disorders in other parts . . . nervous, circulatory, hormonal, etc., could react on sexual health and efficiency.

THE MALE REPRODUCTIVE SYSTEM (Fig. 1)

In the human male the main reproductive organs are outside the pelvic cavity. These are the *penis,* known as the organ of generation, the copulatory organ; and the *testicles* (two), in which spermatozoa and the male hormone are produced.

Inside the pelvis are the *prostate gland,* and two small glands known as *Cowper's glands*. The alkaline fluid secreted by the prostate is a vital component of semen; it also protects the spermatozoa from destructive effects of urine, which is acid.

Cowper's glands also secrete an alkaline fluid which acts as a neutralizer, protecting the sperm, and as a lubricant in intercourse.

The testicles, contained in the *scrotum,* and hanging behind the penis, are a marvel of delicate construction, a fine system of blood vessels, seminal ducts and vesicles.

The spermatozoa, which is constantly being secreted, is stored in the vesicles, which also contribute a secretion to the semen. From each testicle, the *spermatic cord*, made up of seminal duct and blood vessels, leads into the pelvis, at two points, one on each side of the penis.

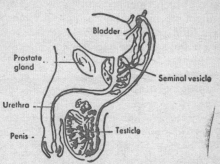

FIG. I MALE REPRODUCTIVE ORGANS

The penis itself is composed of spongy tissues, blood vessels, sensitive nerve ends, small glands and powerful muscles, all protected by a thin loose skin. Since the same passage that conveys the semen—the *urethra*—also conveys urine from the bladder, the penis is provided not only with neutralizing agents but sets of special muscles for ejecting urine or semen, and to constrict the urethra or raise the penis in erection. It is by developing extraordinary control over some of these muscles that yogis may practise the retention of semen described in chapter 3.

Ancient Indian writers on sex divided men into different types, according to the length of the erect penis . . . the Hare man, who is short and thin with a penis of 3½ inches; the Bull man, solid and strong (4½ inches), and the Horse man, tall and muscular (6 inches).

In yogic and Tantric texts the penis is known as *linga** or sometimes *vajra* (thunderbolt). The area between testicles and anus is called *yoni*.

In repose the penis is soft and hangs limply but during

---

* The *linga* is the emblem of Siva, the symbol of life, and as such is worshipped in Indian cults.

sexual excitement the spaces of the spongy or *erectile* tissues become filled with blood, hardening the organ so that it is brought forward and into an upward position by its *erector* muscles. This process is known as *tumescence*. The return to the former flaccid condition, after ejaculation of semen, is called *detumescence*. *Erection* is the erect state.

THE FEMALE REPRODUCTIVE SYSTEM

Since women are designed to protect and nourish the developing foetus in their bodies their organs of generation are set within the pelvic cavity (Fig. 2 and 3). These consist of a right and left *ovary* which produce the female egg-cells; the *fallopian tubes* through which the egg travels to the *uterus* or womb, and the *vagina* or birth canal leading from the uterus to the outside of the body. (The functions of these organs are more fully discussed in Chapter 7, *Yoga and childbirth*). The vagina is also known as the female copulatory organ since it is penetrated by the penis in intercourse.

Due to the vagina's position in the body, its back wall is also the front wall of the anus. Both these passages are supplied with sets of strong muscles.

In yoga and Tantrism the vagina is known as *yoni* or *padma* (lotus).

The main external female genitalia are the folds on each side of the vagina opening (*labium major* and *minor*); the *clitoris,* at the point where these folds meet above the opening, and the *perineum,* at the opposite, lower side. The space between vagina and anus is also known as *yoni*.

The clitoris is often described as an undeveloped penis, having similar components that cause it to enlarge and become erect during sexual excitement, and glands that secrete protective and lubricating fluid.

The ancient books classified women as: the Lotus-woman, fair, soft and plump, graceful, clever and devout, whose sex organs resemble the lotus bud and are scented like a lily; the Art-woman, who is slim, coquettish, pleasure-loving and not highly sexed, whose sex organs smell of honey; the Conch-woman, who is large, rather hairy, passionate, 'hard-hearted, insolent and nagging'. Her organs have a salty smell. The fourth is the Elephant woman, who is short and broad with large hips, throaty voice and a slow, slouching walk. Her characteristic smell is like that of an elephant and she takes a long time to attain sexual satisfaction. The different scents mentioned

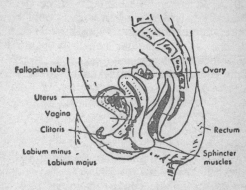

FIG. 2 FEMALE REPRODUCTIVE SYSTEM

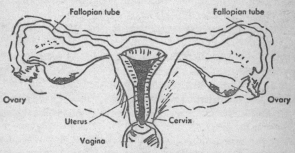

FIG. 3 FEMALE REPRODUCTIVE ORGANS

are believed to refer to the secretions of the apocrine glands, near the sex organs, which vary in physical types as well as in different races.

Both men and women possess mammary glands, (breasts), though in the male these are not developed;

and in both, the sex organs are surrounded with hair to protect them from perspiration and prevent discomfort from friction during intercourse.

No matter how remarkable or well-developed, the reproductive organs are of little use without 'fuel' or driving power. As the lungs are useless without air and the whole body without *prana* or vital energy, so the reproductive system is dependent upon the mind and the glands of the endocrinal system. Mental disturbances could be responsible for anything from frigidity and impotence to savage sex murders, while glandular imbalance could result in physical sexual infantilism, pathologically excessive sexual drive or complete absence of sexuality. In between these extremes are many shades and degrees of sexual disorders.

THE ENDOCRINAL GLANDS

The subject of the endocrinal glands must be included in any discussion of either yoga or sex. They are not only closely associated with the body's sexual activity but are the focus of much attention in yoga training. Many of the most important *asanas* are designed to improve and maintain glandular activity.

Those with which we are most concerned here are the *pituitary;* the *pineal;* the *thyroid* and *parathyroids;* the *adrenal* or suprarenals; the sex glands—*testes* in men, *ovaries* in women.

The pituitary and pineal are in the head; the thyroids in the throat area; the suprarenals, which supply adrenalin, in the small of the back; the testes in the testicles, the ovaries on each side of the pelvis, towards the groin. (The thymus gland, in the chest, normally ceases activity with physical maturity.)

Though the glands work separately, they must also work together in harmony if body and mind are to function normally. All contribute, in varying degrees, to active sex life. The gonads (sex glands) are concerned with reproduction, sex attraction, development of male or female characteristics; the adrenals with energy and activity. The thyroids regulate metabolism, weight, vitality. The pineal is the 'harmonizer' of the system and the pituitary is the most vital and powerful of all.

It is no longer believed that the sex glands alone affect sex life. We now know that a disorder in a key gland—such as pituitary or thyroid—could adversely affect sexual activity. If an infant rat is castrated its sexual growth will be drastically affected; if castration takes place after maturity its sexual powers could continue for some time, providing the pituitary has not been damaged. If the pituitary is removed there will be an immediate cessation of sexual activity.

The pituitary, working through the sex glands, is also believed to control the rhythm of reproductive cycles . . . the most favourable time for fertilization . . . (the period known with animals as 'in season' or 'on heat').

The importance of harmonious working among the glands is frequently demonstrated in women during change of life. At this time the endocrinal system could be completely out of balance, resulting in much mental and physical distress. Depression, sudden rages, hot flushes, increase or loss of weight, excessive libido (sexual desire) in various forms are the most common symptoms.

The glands also have a vital influence on bodily growth and development. If one or other does not function properly the results could be disastrous. If, for instance, a child's pituitary is removed or damaged not only will the sex glands remain undeveloped but the growth of the body will stop. If the balance of hormones is not correct, the result could be anything from a hermaphrodite to a homosexual. All normal men have some feminine hormones, all women possess some male. 'Normality' depends on hormone balance.

Hormonal imbalance could also cause impotence or frigidity in adults; or at the other extreme, such conditions as nymphomania or satyriasis.

EFFECTS OF YOGA ON THE REPRODUCTIVE SYSTEM

There are various ways in which a knowledge of physical yoga could benefit both male and female reproductive systems at different stages of life.

We have mentioned the powerful influence of the endocrinal glands on sexual growth and activity; and to this must be added the importance of a healthy central nervous system, efficient blood circulation, adequate supply of vital energy, and mental and emotional balance, if a satisfactory sex-life is to be enjoyed. All those necessary attributes could be favourably influenced by yoga; also many problems of puberty, menstruation, married life, pregnancy and childbirth, menopause, sexual ageing.

PUBERTY

In humans, as in animals and plants, the main body develops before the reproductive organs mature. The period during which this maturity takes place is known as *puberty*. It is the time when the sexless child begins the physical change to male or female. *Adolescence* is the process of becoming adjusted to these changes, of psychic and emotional adaptation to adult life and newfound sexuality.

The age of puberty varies according to climate, race, diet, even individuals. It usually begins earlier in girls than in boys. Though some weather it with comparative ease and a minimum of disturbance, for others it is a time of great difficulty, bringing psychological and emotional as well as physical upheavals which may result in confusion and uncertainties that have often led to delinquency.

When we consider what takes place in the body during puberty, and the rate at which some of these changes occur it is surprising that more young people are not thrown off-balance by the process. The endocrinal system becomes extremely active, the pituitary, sex glands and adrenals putting out the extra hormones needed to develop the reproductive organs and the so-called secondary sexual characteristics. The child finds his or her body changing in appearance; there may be embarrassing symptoms such as acne, nervous flushing, social uncertainty. For girls there is the sudden appearance of menstruation; for boys there is the sometimes prolonged breaking of the voice. There may be erotic dreams, nocturnal emission of semen in sleep—both of which could cause distress and shame to sensitive children, strictly brought up. Further causes for worry might be a tendency to practise masturbation and sometimes homosexual attractions.

Though such developments are usually transient the sufferer is not always aware of this fact. He or she may have heard or read frightening stories of the fate of masturbators,* may endure great secret misery at the thought of being abnormal in some way. Knowledge which relieves the mind, could in many cases be supported by physical measures to help adjust glandular, nervous or circulatory problems.

If everyone were brought up to regard the sex impulse as a normal part of life, if it were not associated with shame, with religious or other taboos, given exaggerated emphasis or exploitation in films, books, magazines, etc., many difficulties of adolescence might never arise.

But since the majority do grow up in far from ideal conditions, the next best thing is to concentrate upon all possible ways of lessening these dangers and difficulties.

Apart from education to develop a sane healthy attitude to sex, sublimation in various forms is extremely important. It is not suggested that teenagers should practise such sublimative techniques as described in Chapter 2, but that alternative and beneficient channels should be found for troublesome sex energy. This has long been recognized and is the intention behind organized sport in schools and youth movements. This drawing off of surplus energy in games should be supplemented by directing the mind into creative channels, artistic or in some way constructive. Such training is not only a form of sublimation but lays the foundation for a life full of interest.

Hatha yoga, with its physical and mental disciplines, develops strength of character as well as muscles. *Asanas* which act directly on the endocrinal glands help to stabilize some of the disturbing fluctuations of puberty; others bring grace and suppleness, coordination of movement; others again keep the internal organs and circulation healthy and properly functioning. Body-moulding exer-

* Most of these tales of impotence, insanity, etc., have been exploded by medical science. Greater dangers of masturbation are the sense of guilt, of being 'different', perhaps inferior, and the selfish and anti-social attitude said to result from the practice.

cises influence weight and proportions, correct breathing improves complexion, vital energy and nervous system, while the physical challenges offered by the training, the feeling of mastery over the body give confidence and help dispel shyness and gaucherie. For the more thoughtful adolescent, yoga philosophy could bring a sense of peace and perspective on life.

SUGGESTED ASANAS

Head Pose (plate 8, in insert), Shoulderstand (plate 1, in insert), Half-Shoulderstand (plate 2, in insert), Pose of Tranquillity (plate 3, in insert), *Uddiyana* (plate 27, in insert), *Nauli* (plate 28, in insert). Bow Pose (plate 23, in insert), Cobra (plate 21, in insert), Locust (plate 22, in insert), Spinal Twist (plate 26, in insert), Archer (plate 36, in insert), Balancing Poses (page 129–0), Breathing Cycles (page 139–42), All crosslegged poses (pages 125, 126, 127).

MENSTRUATION

Menstruation in women, which starts with puberty and lasts till the menopause, is the body's means of discharging unfertilized ova or egg-cells produced by the ovaries. This usually happens every twenty-eight days, as the name, from the Latin *menses* (month) suggests, though individual variations and irregularities are common.

During the month the uterus prepares to receive the ovum, should conception have taken place. A thickened lining is built up in which the fertilized egg becomes embedded and where it stays during pregnancy, when menstruation stops. When conception has not occurred, this lining breaks down and is discharged from the body with the unfertilized egg.

During puberty and the menopause menstruation is often irregular, but in the former case usually regulates itself without treatment and in the latter gradually tapers off and finally ceases. Other kinds of irregularity could come from internal growths, (fibroids, cysts, cancer, etc.), diseases (such as anaemia, tuberculosis) or hormonal disturbances. For this reason continued menstrual trouble should always be referred to a doctor.

Though most healthy women have little trouble with menstruation, others may experience nervousness, depression, irritability before and during a period, or local pain and headache severe enough to keep them in bed for a day or two. Pain may also be caused by mental disturbances, worry, anxiety, grief, intense jealousy . . . by chronic constipation, by constant sexual excitement without satisfaction, by diseases or displacements of reproductive organs or by hormonal disorders. Backache is common, and a nagging, dragging-down pain in the lower abdomen in the area of the ovaries, even in the legs. All cases of severe pain should be medically investigated.

The hormones which most directly influence menstruation are produced in the ovaries but the pituitary and thyroid glands also contribute. When there is no disease or indication of cysts or other growths, and if medical approval is given, many cases of irregularity or of excessive pain could be improved by the yoga *asanas* that affect these glands.

The following are suggested, though they should not be practised *during* the period: *Uddiyana; Nauli;* Bow; Cobra; Eagle; Headstand; Shoulderstand; Fish pose; all to tone-up reproductive organs and related glands. For pre-menstrual tension, *Savasana,* Pacifying breathing-cycles and Pose of Tranquillity. General practice will strengthen and improve the health and help combat fatigue, aches and pains.

MENOPAUSE IN MEN AND WOMEN

The menopause or change of life in women could start as early as the mid-thirties though more often it is in the mid-forties or fifties. It marks the end of the child-bearing period and brings certain changes in the body, particularly in the endocrinal system. As the egg-producing functions of the ovaries begin to decline other glands take over in compensation. The process is sometimes quick, sometimes protracted and may cause physical and mental disturbances.

In the past when women were less informed on sex matters these miseries were usually endured without help or understanding. Ignorance added fear and dread. Many believed change of life meant change of sex. Old-wives'-tales and horror stories abounded, of women developing beards, deep bass voices, loss of feminine attraction. Cancer, even insanity were said to come at this time. There were no hormone pills or injections to help smooth out the glandular change, no methods of relaxing frayed nerves and discharging menopausal tension, no therapeutic and beneficial exercises; and at the end of this disagreeable, even tragic period was the spectre of old age.

It is no longer necessary to suffer blindly. Women now know—or could easily find out—what is happening to their bodies, why they experience distressing symptoms, and in many cases, how they could help themselves.

An increasing number have turned to yoga. An Australian women's magazine which recently published a series of articles on different ways of 'beating the menopause' concluded with the opinion that this was the safest effective method. The journalist interviewing middle-aged women uncovered a variety of experiences.

A typical case was a woman of forty-five with three teenage children, who had endured acute mental and physical suffering. Afflicted with profuse and erratic periods, headaches and nervous tension she had gone from one doctor to another, taken all kinds of medicines which did not agree with her, and hormone treatments which depressed her, until the doctor, losing patience, told her nothing more could be done and she must just grin and bear it.

Although very good-looking, she had developed negative complexes about her figure, dressing, even personality, all of which had helped poison her attitude to life. She was moody, unreasonably irritable, full of self-pity. Her family life was affected. She had turned against sex, alienated her husband and was persecuting her only son to such an extent that his father had threatened to take him away.

She was brought—reluctantly—to a yoga class by a

friend who had found it helped her in the menopause. She started apathetically, without confidence in herself or the remedy; but her attitude changed and after six months of determined effort there was a striking improvement in health, appearance and outlook. These were reflected in her personal life. To watch this woman's progress was extremely encouraging, but even better was to receive a visit from her husband, who came to tell us of the changes in their family life.

Though yoga had restored this woman's vitality, good looks, peace of mind and domestic happiness, it must be emphasized that it was through her own desire to be helped, her courage and perseverance that the method was able to give this help.

Another student had had an induced menopause with radium. Eighteen months after starting yoga practice she was alarmed to find bleeding had recommenced. The specialist found her body was so rejuvenated that the shrivelled ovaries were trying to work again.

Many other cases of rejuvenation have been recorded.

The most common mental disturbances of menopause are depression, self-pity, jealousy of younger women, loss of confidence, irritability; while hot flushes, headaches, exhaustion, insomnia, tension, constipation, indigestion and flatulence, and profuse irregular periods are frequent physical manifestations.

Yoga relaxation, pacifying and energy-charging breaths are important in overcoming tension, 'nerves' and fatigue. The Shoulderstand, working through the thyroid gland, discourages hot flushes; the Headstand stimulates the pituitary hormones which help compensate for fading ovaries and restore glandular balance; Cobra, Bow and Fish poses stimulate adrenal glands; *Uddiyana* and *Nauli* correct menstrual troubles as well as improving digestive and eliminative processes. Knee-to-stomach Pose reduces flatulence; while Triangular Pose, *Savasana* and Pacifying Breaths improve sleep. Physical improvement is often quickly reflected in mental outlook.

If commonsense living, plenty of rest, fresh air, exercise, light but nourishing diet without stimulants . . .

above all a busy, active life are added to practice many of these discomforts will be greatly relieved.

In men, change of life more often shows in uncharacteristic depression, self-doubt, irritability, loss of confidence, a heightened sense of mortality, of life's brevity. There may be a decline in sexual desire (libido); the man may be filled with thoughts of happiness missed, of frustration, disenchantment; he may become restless, filled with a sudden urge to make up for lost time, to prove he is still young. The personality may be so changed that friends and family 'don't know what has come over him'. In extreme cases perversion may flare out . . . homosexual tendencies, exhibitionism, attraction towards juveniles. Some psychiatrists believe that these are not so much changes as buried desires released by a generally lowered resistance—psychic, moral and physical. Though they could cause great misery, even scandal and tragedy, they are usually transient.

A common tendency is the pursuit of much younger women. Ageing men could often renew themselves sexually with a fresh, younger partner. History has many tales of beautiful girls brought to the beds of elderly sultans and kings for such remedial purposes; but this rejuvenation is only temporary, and apart from the psychological clashes of winter-spring partnerships, could end in greater unhappiness than before. (The old idea that ageing men prefer inexperienced girls as being less likely to detect and criticise failing sexual powers rather lacks conviction in these days of juvenile sex enlightenment.)

It is possible for an older man to fall deeply in love . . . as with Goethe, for instance . . . and suffer intensely, even to the point of death; it is also possible for him to make a quite happy marriage with a comparatively young woman. Cases are entirely individual, depending not only on the man's sexual virility and efficiency but his mental attitude and outlook on life; the degree to which he has retained his health and vital energy.

Physically, change of life in men most frequently manifests in insomnia, in inexplicable chronic fatigue, sometimes backache or vague aches and pains in other parts of the body, enlargement of the prostate gland and impotence.

Prostate trouble should be reported to a doctor but in the early stages it could be relieved by *Aswini mudra* (page 128), Solar-plexus Pose (plate 30, in insert), Frog pose (plate 13, in insert), Arch gesture (plate 32, in insert) and massage given on page 113-14.

Impotence is discussed on page 90.

YOGA AND DISORDERS OF THE REPRODUCTIVE SYSTEM

The most common sexual disturbances brought to the attention of yoga teachers are impotence in men (page 90), menstrual irregularities (see page 72) and after-effects of hysterectomies in women, and failing libido in both sexes. Other disorders are premature ejaculation (page 90), prostate enlargement, prolapse of the uterus and sterility (page 91).

To a certain extent, physical yoga could improve all these conditions.

HYSTERECTOMIES*

At one time this operation was considered a rather extreme measure but the number of women who have been subjected to it suggests that it may now have replaced removal of tonsils or appendix in surgical fashions. There are, of course, cases when it is necessary but too often there is the attitude that a woman in her forties, with several children, no longer needs her reproductive organs.

A steady trickle of baffled, unhappy, sometimes desperate women find their way to yoga class with the same story: they were assured there would be no change at all . . . they would feel better and younger and more active . . . but now they feel ten times worse, with hot flushes, extreme depression, giddiness, palpitations, complete loss of energy and interest in life. They cry for no reason, suffer unbearable tension, burst into insane rages, cannot sleep—in short, are enduring all the symptoms of menopause at once. The whole glandular balance has been vio-

---

* Though this word, correctly, refers to 'cutting into the uterus' it is popularly misused to cover removal of ovaries and uterus.

lently upset. A process that nature effects slowly and gradually has been thrust upon an unprepared body and mind. Psychological effects could be even more drastic for there is often intense bitterness and resentment, a feeling of having been cheated, that the operation could perhaps have been avoided.

Sometimes the bewildered woman is told that her new disturbing symptoms are just Change of Life which she would have had anyway; that it will pass, and she must just put up with it. Some doctors make the transition more bearable by hormone therapy but others distrust or cannot give it for varying reasons. Others again prescribe tranquillizers and sleeping pills on which the patient soon becomes dependent.

A number of doctors now advise these unhappy women to take up yoga.

Yoga cannot put back ovaries that have been removed or stimulate glands that no longer exist, but it can increase the efficiency of those that remain and which, as we know, gradually take over and replace the work of the ovaries. Adrenals, pituitary and thyroid could all be brought to maximum state of health and efficiency through Cobra, Bow, Locust, Headstand and Shoulderstand poses, while many menopausal disturbances are alleviated by the practice suggested on page 73.

Though women should always seek medical advice for sudden inexplicable pain, discharge or bleeding—which could be a sign of cancer—there have been many cases where the condition was rectified by yoga to the stage where even curettes were unnecessary, let alone more drastic surgery.

PROLAPSE OF THE UTERUS

This displacement, usually caused by muscular weakness, perhaps after excessive child-bearing, is encountered in women of any age. Though it is often corrected by surgery, some doctors now recommend exercise in the early stages to tighten the muscles.

In practising yoga to correct prolapsed uterus, all move-

PLATE 1 Shoulderstand

PLATE 2 Half-shoulderstand

PLATE 3 Pose of Tranquility

PLATE 4 Choking pose

PLATE 5
Bound Shoulderstand

PLATE 6   Bound plough

PLATE 7
Balancing shoulderstand

PLATE 8 Head pose

PLATE 9 Inverted Eagle

PLATE 10 Inverted Tree

PLATE 11 Half-lotus

PLATE 12 Pose of a Hero

PLATE 13 Pose of a Frog

PLATE 14 *Yoga-mudra*

PLATE 15 Dangerous pose

PLATE 16 Pose of a Tree

PLATE 17 Pose of an Eagle

PLATE 18 Knee-foot pose

PLATE 19 Angular pose

PLATE 20 Half-Mountain pose

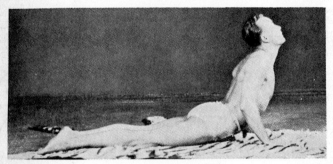

PLATE 21 Pose of a Cobra

PLATE 22 Pose of a Locust

PLATE 23 Pose of a Bow

PLATE 24 Supine Pelvic

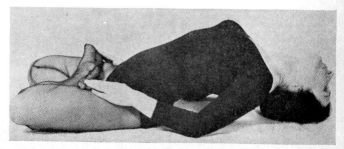

PLATE 25 Pose of a Fish

PLATE 26 Spinal Twist

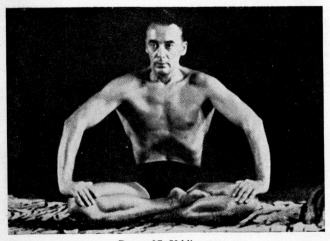

PLATE 27 *Uddiyana*

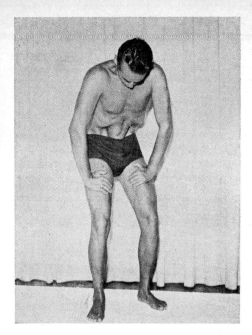

PLATE 28
Nauli

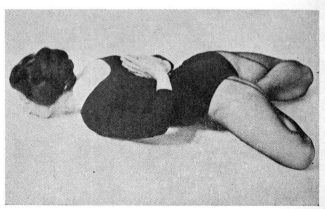

PLATE 29 Hidden *padmasana*

PLATE 30 Solar plexus pose

PLATE 31 Pose of a Star

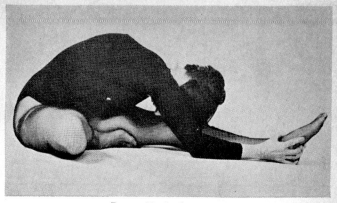

PLATE 32 Arch gesture

PLATE 33 Splits pose

PLATE 34 Scales pose

PLATE 35 Sideways swing

PLATE 36 Pose of an Archer

ments and *asanas* involving sudden and strenuous contraction of or stress on stomach muscles must be avoided. The most beneficial poses are Headstand, Shoulderstand and other inverted positions. Also *Aswini-mudra*.

SEXUAL AGEING

The cause of sexual ageing is not yet fully understood. Some authorities suggest that it is largely psychological, others that it is the automatic accompaniment to general ageing; but all agree that it involves a reduction of male and female homones in the system.

As we know, the sex hormones are responsible for the male or female characteristics of the body which begin to appear at puberty. We also know that each man contains some female hormones and each woman some male hormones and that in normal men the male predominates while the female predominates in women. As a man's body ages, his male hormone will decrease while his female hormone increases, if the glands are not kept young and healthy. Not only does his male sex urge diminish but he may change in appearance, losing some of his more masculine characteristics. The same process takes place in ageing female glands. This is why old women often resemble old men and vice versa.

Even in youth the endocrinal glands are frequently not working to full capacity. Increasing age, with its reduction in physical exertion and healthy exercise further impairs their efficiency. The result could be excess weight, depression, apathy, loss of energy and diminished interest in sex.

At one time it was thought that when a woman's ovaries ceased producing egg-cells her sex life was over. It is now suggested that to a great extent the hormone needed for sexual response comes from the adrenal glands which are not affected by the menopause, unless to increase their output in compensation for the ovaries. Since the adrenals may be kept toned-up by yoga practice this could contribute notably to their continued activity.

It was also thought—and by some is still believed—that general ageing automatically meant decreased libido and the end of sex life; but modern investigators now claim that this need not happen if vitality and healthy glands are maintained.

Loss of sexual desire could come from many causes other than ageing . . . hormone deficiency; sexual debility; excessive worry, anxiety, grief; mental inhibitions (fear, guilt, complexes, etc.); constitutional weakness or disease in another part of the body; a general decline in health through lack of fresh air and exercise. It could result from intense intellectual or creative activity—an unconscious transmutation of energy; it could come from prolonged celibacy and sublimation in youth; it could mean no more than that the body needs a temporary rest from sex.

None of these conditions are insurmountable. Many of the physical causes could be eliminated and libido maintained right through life by intelligent practice. Vital energy is essential and must be increased, accumulated and conserved by improved breathing and recharging techniques; the glands must be kept in best possible condition —(Headstand, Shoulderstand, Cobra, Bow, Eagle and Locust); nervous tension must be discharged and mental strain released—(*Savasana,* Pacifying Breaths, Pose of Tranquillity). The whole standard of health must be raised and sustained by breathing exercises and general practice to improve mobility, circulation, digestion and elimination.

A recent ironic case of rejuvenation and restoration of libido through yoga was a middle-aged widow who had finished the menopause and was settling down to a sexless existence. Yoga so toned-up her ageing glands that menstruation restarted and a revived, inconvenient need for sex life.

Regular medical inspections are always advisable in middle age—essential if unfamiliar symptoms appear—but when there is no serious condition to forbid it both men and women could profit from yoga as they grow older. It not only keeps them active and healthy but helps a graceful transition to what we call Old Age, but which should really be autumnal ripeness. This could be the best time of life, if freed of many material responsibilities and domestic ties we enjoy good health, the new energy that comes after the menopause, and a serene philosphical mind.

6

Yoga and Married Life

Male and female sex anatomy. Necessity for adjustments in intercourse. Coital postures. Exercises recommended to increase sexual efficiency and facilitate variation in coital postures.

To limit sex to a purely mechanical bodily act, divorcing it from emotional, mental and spiritual life, is to deny man his human status. For sensitive, thinking men and women intercourse must be more than the simple act of coitus. For them the process of loving, the longing for psychic and spiritual as well as physical contact, cannot be explained merely as a means of increasing tumescence, the preliminary to successful ejaculation of semen for the purpose of procreation. Affection, tenderness, personal selection, which are found in all types and races, as well as among many birds and animals, must be present.

Sex, illumined by love, has been the inspiration of many of the world's greatest works of art, heroic acts, sublime thoughts; yet, as we know, the qualities . . . sensitivity, imagination, devotion . . . which thus ennoble nature's basic purpose are often the cause of human downfall. At the same time, so strange are the effects of civilization, one of our most natural and fundamental instincts—the drive to reproduction—has also become a cause of unhappiness.

Neither god nor animal but a little of each, man's suffering is often caused by his inability to reconcile these two conflicting strains; but human love demands a balance between god and animal, spirit and flesh. A love that is entirely spiritual is no more complete than sex without affection.

Because sex is a natural function it is often said to require no tuition. Love-making is compared to eating, which, we are reminded, we do by instinct. It is true that a hungry man eats instinctively; but it is also true that feeding, purely to refuel the body, is dull and monotonous and often brings digestive upsets and disorders. As the enjoyment of good, well-prepared food results in greater physical, mental and aesthetic satisfaction, so knowledge and skill in the sexual act brings increased happiness.

Man could, of course, reproduce himself blindly, like amoeba and worms. The race would go on; but since he is neither amoeba nor worm, his more subtle needs would not be supplied. Sooner or later he would become dissatisfied, disappointed, disturbed. The brain, which has raised him from the animals, turns against its betrayer and takes revenge, in conscious unhappinesss, even violence; or more insidiously, through the central nervous system, as mental or physical disorders.

It is said that women are more prone than men to such neuroses and hypochondria; that through natural reticence they accept sexual maladjustments and seek consolation in children or social life; that being more inhibited they are less likely to ask medical help or experiment with other partners. Whether or not this is true, the imaginary invalids, restless socialites, petulant, ever-dissatisfied, whining or nagging women so often encountered are frequently objects of pity rather than condemnation.

Most yoga teachers receive a number of confidences—physical, mental, emotional—from women trying to save unhappy marriages. Sometimes these women seek help in developing a more philosophical outlook, more strength to carry on; others hope to improve their physical appearance and attractions; others again, to become 'a more interesting person', and thus gain their husband's respect. Some are groping for a kind of spiritual independence; others do not know what they are searching for; they are desperate. Those who are really anxious to help themselves usually find, in varying degrees, the support they need. It manifests in different ways—an increased patience and endurance, in greater tolerance and compassion; or perhaps as the power of inner withdrawal in the face of insurmountable, inescapable situations.

Physical problems are usually less complex. Some result from lowered health and vitality, others from ignorance of sex anatomy or inability to make needed adjustment in coitus.

There are various ways in which physical yoga could improve and help maintain sexual potency and efficiency in men and women.

1. By raising the standard of general health, thus providing the maximum favourable conditions; and in certain cases providing a means of correcting disorders that prevent enjoyment of coitus.

2. By increasing vital energy, which leads to greater joy in living, more powerful libido, increased potency and ability to prolong coitus.

3. By toning-up the endocrinal glands that influence sexual functions.

4. By relaxing nervous tension, thus reducing anxieties that could contribute to impotence, premature ejaculation, frigidity and other inhibitions.

5. By toning-up the roots of spinal nerves and improving the health of the central nervous system through exercise and self-massage.

6. By increasing suppleness in joints and pelvis, leading to greater sexual efficiency and enjoyment.

7. By teaching control of muscles in the sexual areas, leading to greater sexual efficiency and restoring tone to vaginal muscles grown slack through childbirth or other causes.

8. By improving physical attractions . . . figure, complexion, vitality, personal magnetism.

9. By increasing confidence through exercise, relaxation and improved breathing.

These benefits might be compared with the eight items listed in *The Perfumed Garden* as favouring coition: . . . 'health, freedom from worry, absence of preoccupation, a gay disposition, a generous diet, wealth, and variety in the features and complexion of the woman.'

Since methods of practices for raising the standard of health, increasing vital energy, toning-up glands and relaxing nervous tension are discussed elsewhere in this book the main emphasis here is on improving sexual efficiency. Such improvement demands a knowledge of sex anatomy and the mechanics of intercourse.

Before coitus can take place there must be what is known as tumescence. Though this is common to both sexes, it is more obvious and more imperative in the male.

In the male, tumescence is the process by which the spongy erectile tissues in the penis become filled with blood, the glands secrete lubricating and protective fluids, the penis hardens and is raised by its erector muscles. It is usually set in motion by impulses from the brain, transmitted through the spinal cord and sexual centre in the spine, but it also works in reverse; i.e. local stimulation of sex organs sends impulses to the brain which registers sensations of pleasure. As already mentioned, impulses going out to the sex centre from the brain are first aroused there by stimuli received through the senses . . . sight, touch, smell, etc. Disorders or weaknesses in one set of bodily functions therefore could react unfavourably on sexual activity.

In the female, tumescence is basically the same. The sexual organs become swollen with blood, the glands secrete lubricating fluids, the clitoris erects. There is even a form of ejaculation, though not to the same extent as in the male. This is the female seed, *rajas,* lotus dust referred to in yoga and Tantric texts.

The time taken for this process varies according to individuals and circumstance. If a man is deeply in love, or the partners are mutually attracted it will be shorter than when there is little attraction or interest; but all healthy civilized humans achieve tumescence more rapidly than wild animals, for whom prolonged and spectacular displays must sometimes precede intercourse. Even hermaphrodite slugs indulge in complex and fantastic manoeuvres before their curious mating.

Courtship is a more poetic name for tumescence, which is not, as is sometimes imagined, merely a sentimental and unnecessary trimming. It is, or should be, an integral preliminary, if intercourse is to be satisfactory for both partners, and should, in an abbreviated form, precede each act of union. The male bird or animal, dancing, parading before the female is not only working himself up for coitus but is also attracting, exciting her to a similar state of response. In humans the principle is the same. Much is now written about the fact that women take longer than men to arouse sexually; that frequently the male partner has reached orgasm and ejaculation before the female has had time to respond and that this is a common cause of unhappiness and marital failure. Ability to make the woman physically, emotionally, psychically receptive would save much of this unhappiness.

'The prolongation of the preliminary courtship, before the act,' wrote Havelock Ellis, 'is necessary on the physical side, in order to ensure tumescence; it is necessary on the psychic side because without it the ideal element of love, which is essential to real marriage, cannot well be developed.'

Though tumescence is normally a fairly rapid process it may be subject to difficulties. Apart from boredom, lack of attraction in the partner or other psychological reasons it could be inhibited by poor health, lack of vitality, hormone deficiency, nervous tension and lack of confidence.

In the male, intercourse brings tumescence to its highest peak, culminating in orgasm and ejaculation of semen, and is followed by detumescence. Theoretically the process should be the same for both sexes, but since women are technically capable of intercourse without either tumescence or orgasm and since even now there are many who are ignorant of their sexual 'rights' or too shy to discuss them, the performance is often a one-sided affair . . . Sexologists, marriage counsellors, psychiatrists know just how often.

Surveys on sex behaviour have frequently emphasized that many women have never experienced orgasm. Though there is still a difference of opinion whether this takes place mainly through vagina or clitoris, it is generally accepted that the latter plays a vital part, and that for coitus to be satisfactory this organ must receive stimulation. Ideally, having become 'erected' or tumescent by courtship (love-play), it is further excited by pressure and movement of the male pubis during intercourse, eventually to the state of climax or orgasm. The degree to which it receives this pressure and movement depends on its position in relation to the vaginal opening; but even if it is set too 'high', too far from this orifice, it could be brought to the most favourable position by varying coital posture.

Coital variations are sometimes regarded as a form of perversion. Different countries, religions, communities have their own ideas of orthodoxy and distrust or fear any departure from what they hold 'normal'. Though psychologically it could be harmful to indulge in practices that are believed wrong or sinful, re-education of this attitude could lead to correction of many physical maladjustments, and to greater happiness. We cannot do better than quote Havelock Ellis on this contentious subject: 'The recognition that a number of methods of intercourse, far from being vicious 'perversions', come within the normal human range of variation, is required because it is often found that when one method is unsuitable to secure gratification another method proves more successful. Taking sexual relationships in the widest sense, but still on the physical side, it is important always to bear in mind that whatever gives satisfaction and relief to both parties is good and right, and even in the best sense normal, provided . . . no injury is effected.'

We would only qualify 'injury' with 'mental or physical', since a sense of guilt is essentially destructive to healthy sex-life.

Though sex books, particularly ancient Eastern works on the art of love, sometimes claim to list hundreds of coital positions, most are variations on a few basic postures. In these, both man and woman may be lying or sitting or standing; they may lie face-to-face, with man or woman on top; or on their sides, face-to-face, or with the woman's back to the man. One may lie on the back, the other on the side; one may lie while the other kneels; they may sit or stand face-to-face, or both facing the same way; they may indulge in kneeling, bending or stretching, taking weight on fore-arms, elbows, knees. The back may be subjected to unaccustomed stress, the joints obliged to take up unfamiliar positions.

The main purpose of such variations is to ensure satisfaction for both partners; or where no difficulties exist, to break the monotony that is so often blamed for the failure of conjugal happiness.

If the problem to be overcome, for instance, is a clitoris that is placed too 'high' (that does not make contact with the male body in intercourse) the coital pose should laterally stretch the vagina—i.e. broaden it, bringing the clitoris down to the required position. This is best achieved if the woman's thighs are separated, as she lies on her back. It is also a suitable pose when the vagina is too narrow (or penis too thick); or if conception is not desired.

A vagina that is slack or has been stretched will be made narrower if the thighs are kept together.

In pregnancy, or in other conditions where the woman should not take weight on her abdomen, positions on the side will be called for. Lateral, also sitting positions could help overcome great difference in height, or might be best used in cases of illness, weakness or such disabilities as chronic backache or heart conditions, as well as in advanced age. If both partners or one of them are excessively overweight, poses recommended for pregnancy should be used; other postures again facilitate or discourage conception.

Whatever the cause, such manoeuvres demand not only some anatomical knowledge in both partners but supple joints and muscular control. It is little use advising married couples to experiment with coital postures if the participants are so stiff or in such poor condition that they cannot follow instructions, or having followed them are incapable of further activity—apart from aesthetics.

Special exercises for the pelvic area will give greater flexibility and ease of movement without hardening muscles. These movements also promote healthy blood circulation in the reproductive organs and tone up the sex glands.

Slack vaginal muscles could be a cause of unsatisfactory coitus. If they have grown lax from childbirth, lazy habits, obesity, there may be considerable reduction in sensation for both partners. The muscles, however, could be toned up, and trained to compensate for any stretching; also to overcome problems caused by disparity in the size of the sex organs.

From most ancient times the ability to increase pleasure through control of the vaginal muscles has been highly prized. Women slaves thus trained fetched high prices. In Abyssinia there were women known as Holders who could induce orgasm in a man by this technique alone, and some who could so constrict their muscles as to cause pain to their partner.

Certain yoga techniques, originally designed for male use, could be adapted by women for use in obtaining such control.

The vagina has two sets of muscles, a *sphincter* and a *levator* . . . the former to open and close the entrance, the latter to contract and relax the passage itself in an upward-downward movement. Similar muscles are found in the anus, and since in women the back of the vaginal wall is the front wall of the anus there is a certain amount of muscular interplay in this area. Though both sets of muscles work involuntarily they could also be trained to respond to conscious control.

The yoga technique known as *Aswini-mudra* (page 128) gives control of the anal muscles in conjunction with inhalation-exhalation. Women could learn to adapt this practice to the vaginal levator muscles, so that continual contraction and relaxing may be done in quick succession. This is an important pre-natal exercise and also helps restore tone and elasticity after delivery. In coitus, the ability to produce this sensation on the male organ greatly intensifies enjoyment and is also a positive contribution in overcoming such conditions as weak potency. It is also recommended for prolonging coitus. An ancient book compares the movement of the *yoni* on the *linga* to the hand of the *gopi*-girl milking the cow.

Similar adaptation could be made with the abdominal contractions, *Uddiyana* and *Nauli*.

Contraction of the vaginal sphincter muscles in coitus not only helps to hold the penis but draws down the clitoris, thus bringing it into closer contact with the male pubis.

We have so far referred only to female problems. Since the male cannot have intercourse without tumescence, his are of a different nature.

IMPOTENCE

Impotence is said to be increasing in civilized society and may occur in otherwise healthy men. It may be psychic (mental), endocrinal or organic in origin.

Psychic impotence could be caused by inhibitions, guilt, wrong sex education and training in youth, etc.; endocrinal impotence by hormonal deficiency, and organic impotence by disorders of brain and spinal cord, central nervous system, prostate, urethra, atrophy of the testicles, (a possible result of mumps leading to hormone deficiency), kidney disease, diabetes, chronic hypertension or venereal disease in which either the penis is affected or —as in syphilis—the central nervous system.

Since endocrinal impotence means deficiency in hormones not only from the testicles but also thyroid, adrenal and anterior pituitary it could be favourably affected by toning-up these glands, as well as stimulating the circulation and general health.

When organic impotence comes from actual disease there must be medical treatment, but such causes as high blood-pressure and many nervous disorders respond to improved breathing and relaxing of tension. In all cases, better health brought about by general practice is a vital part of treatment. It brings greater vitality and optimism and discourages tendencies to brood and worry about the condition, which in themselves contribute to its persistence.

PREMATURE EJACULATION

Although this is often psychic in origin, it could also be aggravated by constipation, haemorrhoids, congestion of prostate or seminal vesicles or from constant sexual stimulation without gratification, resulting in local irritation and inflammation. (More serious causes could be kidney disease, diabetes.)

Ability to relax nervous tension is extremely important in any cure, and a calmer, more optimistic attitude helps reduce the fear of failure that so often prolongs the complaint. To overcome local contributing disorders, *Uddiyana* and *Nauli* will correct constipation; haemorrhoids will be discouraged by the Headstand and all Inverted Poses; *Aswini-mudra* and the rocking massage on page 113–14.

PAIN AFTER COITUS, IN MALE AND FEMALE

Apart from psychological causes—such as guilt—said to occur in men particularly, coital pain could also come from weak back muscles, poor spinal health, chronic constipation or haemorrhoids.

The *asanas* just recommended should be practiced to correct constipation and haemorrhoids.

The exercises given for greater sexual efficiency (page 95 to 100) will also limber up and strengthen the parts of the body concerned. At the same time there should be general practice for glands, circulation and elimination, to stengthen muscles, loosen joints and relax nervous tension.

In women, pain after intercourse may also stem from displacement of the uterus, inflammation of the vagina, urethra, uterus or ovaries or from ovarian cysts.

Suspected cysts, swellings, discharges or inflammation must be referred to a doctor; but even here some relief could be obtained through muscular and nervous relaxation and correct breathing. For prolapse of the uterus inverted poses are advised.

STERILITY

Though the process of fertilization is generally understood, the causes of sterility are not yet fully known. At one time believed to be peculiar to women, it is now recognized as occurring in both sexes. It may be a temporary state caused by ill-health—e.g. anemia—or general debility; there may be some physical obstruction preventing spermatozoa reaching the ovum; there may be a retroversion of the uterus, hormonal defects, a too-acid vagina

which kills the sperm. The man's semen may contain no
spermatozoa; the woman may not be producing egg-cells
or may have diseased or undeveloped ovaries. The man
and woman may be incompatible, in the context of fertilization. Even faulty diet has been suggested.

Yoga's contribution to correcting sterility comes
through regulation of endocrinal glands, particularly
ovaries and testicles; correction of menstrual disorders;
strengthening the body and improving circulation and
general health. Relaxation of nervous tension is essential
and the ability to cease worrying. Many couples, childless
for years despite every effort, have finally accepted the
fact of sterility and adopted a baby, only to find the wife
pregnant. This is said to result from release of tension
and anxiety.

Asanas to practice: Eagle pose; Shoulderstand; Headstand; Bow; Cobra; Fish; *Aswini-mudra; Uddiyana.*

It has long been believed that when sex fades in marriage it is the woman who has lost interest. At one time
she was thought to have no sex needs at all; until comparatively recently a middle-aged woman was expected to
be more concerned with children or grandchildren than
with sex. Now it is suggested that it is the man who is
responsible for any decrease in marital intercourse; that
men age more quickly than women, who, all things being
equal, could remain at their sexual peak all through the
sixties. Other sexologists believe it is possible for both
sexes to retain potency until the end of life . . . even into
the nineties. This corresponds with the yoga teaching that
the springtime of life is from 55 to 75.

Prolonging potency is no advantage if body and general health have deteriorated through neglect and abuse.
Many women who have been haunted by fear of pregnancy all their married lives find that they and their partners are too tired, too old to enjoy the freedom that
comes after the menopause; on the other hand, those
who have retained their vitality and *joie de vivre* could
find this the best time of all. The words 'autumnal ripeness' come to mind again. Deciduous trees lose their
leaves in winter, but before the leaves fall they burn with

a richness and beauty far deeper than the immature charms of spring. Such a blaze of glory could be within the reach of all who have passed the spring and summer of married life.

DIET

The food of love has long been a favourite subject of speculation and a great deal of nonsense has been written, as well as some common sense. Casanova fed his mistresses oysters; Brillat-Savarin recommends caviar; ancient Eastern writers suggest highly spiced foods to increase potency; fish of all kinds is also recommended by others while modern remedies range from pepper in vodka to raw steak.

Some of these foods are obviously intended as aphrodisiacs and their effects, if any, are temporary; but in others, such as fish, the vitamin content makes a definite contribution to improved health and potency.

Celibates should avoid any such blood-heating foods as spices, red meat, stimulants—tea, coffee, alcohol, etc. The subject of meat is contentious. Male potency does not seem noticeably less in countries where meat is forbidden for religious reasons or is in short supply. In general it would appear that a sensible balanced diet that nourishes every part of the body will also be best for sexual potency and efficiency.

HYGIENE

In hatha yoga, personal cleanliness is not limited to superficial washing of the skin. Internal and external purification is part of the yogi's daily life and many western householders could learn from him in these matters.

Complete washing every day is essential, a bath or shower if possible. Teeth should be cleaned, or at least the mouth washed out after eating; the tongue should be gently scraped of impurities, with an inverted spoon, before the first food or drink of the day. Abdominal contractions to promote internal cleanliness and evacuation of the bowels should be part of the morning routine.

Where sex is concerned, the need for high standards of hygiene is even more important, not only for aesthetic reasons but out of consideration for those intimately concerned. Sensitive people have been repelled in lovemaking by a partner's lack of personal cleanliness. Though the advocates of natural methods (so-called) claim that such finesse is decadent and unnecessary, that animals and primitive men were not so affected, the fact remains that civilized beings are not attracted by unpleasant smells and a slovenly appearance.

The body should be kept scrupulously clean at all times, with particular attention to genital organs. This is imperative before retiring, if two people are sharing a bed. Clothes should be changed frequently, underwear every day. Stale perspiration, bad breath are not conducive to romantic interludes. Some ancient sex books insist that husbands or wives should get up before their partner wakes and wash out the mouth to avoid giving offence.

Women should keep the vagina clean by douching with warm water. This should be done regularly and is specially necessary at the time of menstruation; but sexual hygiene is not limited to women. Many men could improve the cleanliness of their sex organs, keeping them free from traces of urine or glandular secretions which, if left unwashed, give off stale smells. These distasteful evidences of careless hygiene may be noticed even in fully-dressed crowds.

The question of sleeping in separate beds must be decided by individual preference. It is undoubtedly healthier to sleep alone; there is more room for relaxation, less likelihood of infections, of sleep being disturbed; but sometimes it is better to let emotional factors outweigh such considerations. It is more important that both partners agree about fresh air in the room, for this is essential to sound healthy sleep.

EXERCISES TO INCREASE SEXUAL EFFICIENCY

These exercises improve circulation in the reproductive organs, tone-up sex glands, give greater suppleness and mobility of movement.

Ideally, all exercises should be practised regularly and preceded by limbering-up movements, to warm the muscles and by deep breathing cycles. It is a good idea to pause from time to time and practise a few deep slow pacifying breaths (page 141) to avoid exhaustion and the building up of undesirable tension. There should never be any suggestion of forcing or strain at any time. Practise on a carpet, folded rug or foam-rubber mat and ensure that there is plenty of fresh air, but not draughts.

As with *asanas,* never practise immediately after eating. Early morning, just before lunch or just before dinner at night are the best times, if convenient. Usually the body is more supple in the evening, the muscles having been warmed up during the day.

It is inevitable that a number of exercises for sex efficiency and pre-natal health should over-lap since all are designed to increase suppleness in the same part of the body. The reader may therefore select those most suitable from either section.

For exercises to develop control of abdominal and vaginal muscles see *Asanas,* Chapter 8.

FOR WOMEN

1. Standing with feet together or lying on the back. Contract the buttocks, pulling the muscles inward, then relaxing. In this movement the mouth of anus, vagina and muscles of the perineum are also contracted and relaxed.

2. On all-fours, keeping arms straight and palms on the floor, move forward over the arms, then sit back on to the heels; then forward again, then back again. This exercise is more powerful if the movement follows a rhythm . . . forward; back 1–2–3; forward; back 1–2–3. Forward is one movement; back is actually three light pressures of the buttocks against the heels.

3. On all-fours. Arch the back so the pelvis is raised; then relax and lower pelvis. (See Figs. 4a and 4b) Repeat several times. (This movement and the following are variations of the Pose of a Cat. Page 138).

FIG 4A

FIG 4B

4. On all-fours. Swing pelvis to the right side, then to the left. Be sure movement is only from waist down—the front of the body should be stationary. Repeat several times, trying to increase speed of movement.

5. In the same position, rotate the pelvis, moving only from waist down.

6. Sit back on the heels with body bent forward so forehead rests on the floor. Arms are stretched above the head, on the floor. (Fig. 5a and 5b) Raise arms, head, body till you are standing on your knees, and continue movement arching back till arms reach back as far over the heels as possible; then come forward and down again to starting position. This movement resembles a Moslem praying and could be combined with inhaling (coming up and back), exhaling (coming down again).

7. In all-fours position. Bending the elbows, bring fore-

head down to touch the floor, at the same time raising the right leg. Come down and repeat on other side.

8. Squatting with knees wide apart and buttocks above, not resting on, heels. If you are used to exercising you

Fig. 5A

could hold your balance with hands on hips or thighs; otherwise hold on to chair or table. Practise moving the pelvic area forward, then back, slowly and carefully at first, then trying to move more quickly . . . back, forward; back, forward . . .

9. Practice the same movement lying on the right side; then on the left. The easiest way is to draw the stomach

Fig. 5B

in so the pelvis is pulled back, then relax the stomach muscles, pushing pelvis forward.

10. On the back, knees bent, feet flat on the floor, try to separate legs as though against resistance; then bring them together again and repeat. If you cannot produce the feeling of tension and resistance, pull the knees apart with the hands and at same time resist with the legs.

11. Lying on the back, raise only the hips from the floor, then lower.

12. In same position, raise only hips and then try to swing them from side to side, keeping shoulders and feet on the floor.

13. On the back, on floor, (though this is more effective practised on a table starting with legs hanging over the edge). Raise the legs, keeping the knees straight, and describe circles, first inward, then outward.

14. In same position, on floor or table, raise legs, keeping them stiff, and try to pull them flat against the stomach.

15. Sit with knees apart and soles of feet together (see *Pose of a Star*, (plate 31). Holding the toes, roll right back till they touch the floor over the head. Come right forward, then repeat several times.

16. Sit with left leg stretched, right knee drawn up and foot flat on the floor. Pick up right foot with both hands and try to bring the toes up to touch the forehead, then the chin, then the chest. Come down and repeat on other side.

17. Sit with left leg stretched and right knee drawn up, foot flat on the floor. Lean forward, putting right arm under the bent knee and round behind to clasp the left hand behind the back. Inhale, raise right calf parallel with the floor; exhale, bringing right foot to the floor and head down to the left knee. Repeat on other side. (This is practised in the Forward-stretching cycle as a variation of Arch Gesture).

18. Standing with feet wide apart, heels on the floor, arms by the sides. Come forward and down, trying to place the palms flat on the floor, as far back between the feet as possible. The fingers should be facing back-ways (Fig. 6).

FIG. 6   FIG. 7

19. Kneel on the right knee with left leg fully stretched out at the side. Link arms over the head, then swing several times over the stretched leg. Repeat on other side (Fig. 7).

20. Stand with feet together and hands in position of prayer. Keeping left foot flat on the floor, slide the right foot back, with toe pointed, till the right knee almost touches the floor. Practise several times, then repeat on other side (Fig. 8). Practise also the following asanas: Supine-pelvic, Lotus and all poses involving Lotus . . .

FIG. 8

Fish, Hidden *padmasana,* Locked Shoulder-stand, etc.;
Aswini-mudra, Yoga-mudra, Solar-plexus pose.

EXERCISES FOR MEN

Efficiency of the male in intercourse is much influenced
by a healthy and supple spine. A slim stomach and
healthy muscles are also a great advantage. All exercises
that bring about these desired results should be practised,
also to strengthen the buttocks, shoulders and arms. Unlike women, men need to increase the hardness of abdominal and genital muscles.

All the exercises recommended for women should be
practised to give required suppleness and to tone up abdominal and thigh muscles. 'Press-up' movements will develop shoulders and arms. *Asanas* and *mudras* should include *Aswini-mudra, Yoga-mudra* and Solar-plexus Pose,
to increase circulation in the sexual area; Cobra; Locust;
Spinal Twist, for spine, buttocks, abdomen and to stimulate adrenal glands; Headstand for pituitary gland;
Shoulderstand for the thyroid gland, and Recharging cycles to increase vital energy.

7

Yoga and Childbirth

Prenatal influence. Process of conception and pregnancy. Preparation for childbirth. Labour. Exercises recommended to prepare the body for labour, facilitate delivery and restore the figure.

All sects, religions, communities have their own beliefs and practices concerning pregnancy and childbirth.

Though science has not yet discovered a method by which parents may choose the sex of their children, many theories have been put forward as to how it is determined. They range from increasing the alkalinity—or acidity—of the female reproductive passages to putting charms under the pillow; from eating certain herbs or roots to ritual intercourse for the conception of a son.

One Hatha yoga theory is that the child's sex is determined by the nostril-breathing of the parents.

If a man's breathing is studied for twenty-four hours it will be found that breath flows more freely through either left or right nostril at different times. Some people breathe more easily through the right, others through the left. The nostril through which the breath flows more freely is known as the Dominant Nostril.

When the father's right nostril dominates, the sex of the first child will be male; if left is the dominant nostril, it will be female. If the right nostril dominates in both parents the child will be male.

The first child's sex is influenced by the father; but if the mother is younger and more virile than the father the second child's sex could be determined by her breathing. (The same rule applies: when right nostril dominates the

sex is male; when left it is female). The third child is influenced by the mother.

For the ordinary student of yoga this theory offers little
practical help since the dominant nostril can only be de-
tected after prolonged study of *pranayama.*

The Jaina yoga communities, mentioned elsewhere,
place faith in réligious observances. To conceive a son
there should be a ritual intercourse immediately following
menstruation. After the woman has taken her purifying
bath, various rites must be carried out, including the
lighting of three holy fires before the *Jina* image,* into
which husband and wife, reciting *mantras,* make oblations.

Coitus must be 'without passion', purely for the sake of
begetting a child. It is preceded by special preparations
. . . the woman bathes her sex organs with prescribed
mixtures, the man prays to the goddess of the *yoni.* During intercourse he recites prayers and concentrates on the
Jina. There must be a lighted candle, for copulation in
the dark brings poverty; betel nut must be chewed; the
colour green must be worn.

In the third, fifth, seventh and ninth month of pregnancy there are special ceremonies to strengthen, and in
the last one to fatten, the foetus. They involve the singing
of *mantras,* the sounding of drums and bells, the lighting
of holy fires; an arch is built over the doorway and two
vessels full of water set by it; the woman rubs her body
with oil, washes with water, then performs an act of worship holding fruit in her hand. She puts on her ornaments, a girdle inscribed with *mantras,* a charm bracelet.
She goes to the temple with her husband, who puts a
yantra† round her neck. In the final ceremony, performed shortly before the child's birth, to ensure that it
will be a son, she is dressed in new clothes and taken out
from the house at night. Money and sweets are distrib-
uted and *mantras* recited for an easy and successful childbirth.

During the birth, *mantras* are recited and prayers
offered; an astrologer waits while the woman is in labour

---

* *Jina:* 'One who has conquered the worldly passions.'
† *Yantra:* Magical diagram.

so that he may make the child's horoscope at the moment of birth.

PRENATAL INFLUENCE AND EXERCISE

Though we are told that sex is decided at the moment of conception and nothing done afterwards can change it, there is little doubt about prenatal influence on the child's general well-being. Many old wives tales and superstitions have been discarded; pregnant women frightened by a dog no longer believe the child will be born with a dog's head; but even the most rational modern mother knows that in another sense her attitude could subtly affect her child.

An exceptional case of pre-natal influence was demonstrated by a yoga student—a woman grotesquely ugly, with a squat clumsy body and heavy limbs. Behind her unprepossessing façade was a sensitive, highly intelligent personality, full of courage and spiritual strength. She had suffered intensely all her life through her ugliness and when she found herself pregnant determined that her child should not experience the same unhappiness.

She went to live in one of the most beautiful parts of the world, in an idyllic setting, surrounding herself with beauty in every form . . . in nature, in music, poetry, carving, sculpture, painting. She concentrated on the thought of beauty, willing it to her child; and when finally it was born it was beautiful as an angel. It grew into an exquisite, happy girl with perfect features and limbs, a living witness to the power of the mind.

This was an unusual instance, brought about by unusual circumstances and by the strength of the mother's will; but the principle applies in all cases. Though physically the child is well protected in the uterus, we still do not know to what extent it is exposed to its mother's emotional and mental conditions.

We do know, however, that a calm, relaxed mother has an easier pregnancy, easier delivery and less feeding problems. The attainment of this tranquillity is greatly assisted by correct diet, exercise, rest; above all proper breathing and the practice of relaxation. Every ante-natal class and book now prescribes a form of relaxation, usually based on the yoga *Savasana*. Full abdominal breathing is also taught, and exercises to stretch the pelvic floor, strengthen back muscles and make the body supple. Modern women go into training for childbirth, which is an excellent practice, for it is in fact a strenuous physical experience which calls upon many muscles that may never have been fully exerted before. The better the condition of those muscles, the easier will be delivery. There can be few women left who really regard childbirth as an illness.

Nor does maternity necessarily mean the loss of the mother's figure. Though we hear a great deal about the primitive woman's ability to produce children without pain or fuss, because of her well-developed muscles, we hear less of the rapidity with which she ages, the speed with which her figure deteriorates after childbirth. For civilized women this need never happen, if they exercise intelligently.

During pregnancy, to accommodate the growing uterus, the abdominal muscles become stretched. After the child is born they remain enlarged and if nothing is done to prevent it, will sag through loss of tone, often becoming the focus for deposits of fat. These disfigurements, so often seen in lazy, inactive women who overeat, could be countered by combined pelvic exercises and abdominal breathing, which strengthen the muscles as well as increasing supplies of oxygen and vital energy.

Posture is very important in pregnancy. If not correct it could be the source of much trouble in childbirth, as well as afterwards. The habit of standing with the back arched and stomach pushed forward is specially prevalent where there is a slight previous tendency to curvature. At all times the body should be straight, head and neck in line with the backbone, buttocks, muscles, and stomach kept in. The feet should be kept together. If they are turned outwards they may flatten and a sloppy, unsightly walk may result. Good posture not only reduces strain on muscles and helps keep the body in good condition but greatly camouflages pregnancy. Exercises for posture are given on page 114.

During pregnancy, as the foetus grows, there may be shortness of breath in the later stages and full diaphragm breathing may be difficult. In such cases the side breathing positions are recommended: Lying on the left side with the left arm stretched under the head and the left knee drawn up. The right arm lies loosely behind (Fig. 9). The pose should be practised on both sides. It is a yoga sleeping position and is very comfortable in pregnancy.

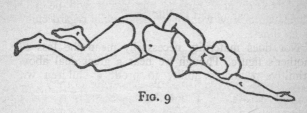

FIG. 9

Exercises for stretching the pelvic floor and pelvic outlet, for toning up muscles and giving great general flexibility will be found on pages 111 to 114. It must be emphasized that no exercising should be undertaken without medical approval. There may be some condition or physical malformation of the uterus that makes it difficult to hold the child. Even when there is no such obstacle and exercising is recommended it must be combined with common sense. Any movements likely to displace the foetus, strenuous upward stretching, raised poses and stomach contractions should be avoided. Every case is is individual. One student for instance, who insisted on practising the headstand every day, against all advice, produced a normal healthy child; others may miscarry at the slightest exertion. In general, most women continue with a modified yoga as long as they comfortably can, but where this is not considered wise practice should be restricted to simple movements, breathing cycles (page 140–2) and relaxation (page 24).

A delightful example was the young mother of a healthy baby who came to yoga because her husband thought she was getting too plump. She continued all through her second pregnancy, in the later stages wearing a short smock over her leotards. The week the baby was due, the class was cancelled because of a public holiday. The following week, the young mother, in her smock, looked particularly radiant but it was not till she lay down to practice *Savasana* that a difference was noticed in her figure. The baby had been born on the public holiday, after half an hour's labour.

To appreciate the importance and purpose of pre-natal exercise it is necessary to understand what takes place during pregnancy and childbirth.

FERTILIZATION AND PREGNANCY

Figs. 2 and 3 (page 67) show the organs of the female reproductive system. From the upper sides of the pear-shaped uterus, the fallopian tubes lead to the ovaries. The narrower uterus base leads into the vagina, the birth canal.

Each month an egg-cell or ovum leaves the ovary and travels to the uterus through the fallopian tubes. In preparation for this cell's arrival, circulation has increased and a thickened lining been built up in the uterus walls. If the cell is not fertilized this lining breaks down and is discharged, with the unfertilized cell, during menstruation; if the cell has been fertilized it embeds itself in the prepared lining where it remains throughout the child's development.

Conception takes place in the fallopian tubes during the ovum's passage to the uterus—which takes about ten days—and results from the union of the female cell with the male cell. Both male and female cells contain forty-eight particles. On entering the fallopian tubes, each throws off half its particles (twenty-four). The male cell pierces the female and injects its remaining twenty-four particles. The female, now complete again within forty-eight, begins the development of the new life, while the male cell, having no particles left, ceases to exist.

By the time the fertilized female cell has reached the uterus it has grown in size, has immunised itself from other male cells and the growth of the baby has begun.

Though the fertilized ovum is minute, it contains materials for the development of the foetus, the placenta or after-birth and the umbilical cord, by which the unborn child receives nourishment. There are also the fluid in which it floats and the membranes to enclose it.

During its development, the foetus receives oxygen from the mother's blood, by way of the placenta, and gives off waste, which is discharged through the mother's circulation and lungs. Correct breathing is therefore very important in pregnancy.

As the uterus increases in size . . . it could grow from 3 to 15 inches . . . it develops extra muscular fibres with which to expel the child during labour. After the third month it also moves upward, till it reaches to below the breast-bone. This is the cause of shortness of breath.

LABOUR

There are three stages in labour: 1. The drawing-up and widening of the uterus neck opening; 2. The passage of the baby through pelvis and birth canal; and 3. The expulsion of the placenta or afterbirth.

During the first stage, the neck of the uterus is drawn right up till the organ is no longer pearshaped . . . (the neck is eventually pulled up over the baby's head). This drawing-up is accompanied by stretching and widening of the opening. At the same time the upper part of the uterus shrinks, becoming thicker and harder, pressing the baby down against the lower part. This also assists the opening process.

During these contractions there is little the mother can do beyond keeping calm and cheerful. Some women like to lie down, others feel better moving about, doing housework, etc. The most important thing, however, is to be completely relaxed, conserving all possible strength for the more active time ahead.

It is now generally accepted that ability to relax during this 'passive' phase, plus an understanding of what is happening, reduces the pain and discomfort which used to be considered inevitable. Fear and anxiety, usually based on ignorance, not only cause rigidity in the uterus muscles, thus protracting the first stage and causing suffering and exhaustion, but glands, alerted by fear, pour out extra hormones to help the body fight the 'emergency'—in this case the mechanical process now in motion. Though the upper uterus automatically continues contracting and pushing, the relaxing and stretching that should correspond in the lower part are now replaced by tensed muscles and resistance. It is this state of deadlock that exhausts the mother.

The second stage of labour is extremely active. When the uterus is fully dilated the contractions change in character, becoming stronger and closer together. There is also an instinct to push or bear down.

To women whose muscles have been toned-up and strengthened by exercise during pregnancy this strenuous phase is stimulating. There is a sense of participation and achievement that is absent from the first stage of labour; in fact the temptation to push too hard or too fast must sometimes be curbed to avoid injury to the child in its passage through the birth canal. Time must also be allowed for the muscles round the vagina mouth to stretch so the baby's head may pass through. Though these muscles are very flexible they will tear if forced too quickly.

The stretching is done by the baby's head which, with each contraction, is pushed against the tissues of the vaginal opening. After the contraction the head recedes, moving down again with the next one, each time slightly enlarging the exit. These tissues could be compared to elastic, which stretches when pulled gently and relaxes when released. If carefully pulled further and further it will stretch right out, but pulled violently, it may snap.

Strong, supple stomach, pelvic and vaginal muscles are an invaluable help in this last part of labour.

On the way through the pelvic area the baby must pass through a jointed ring of bone. If the head is big it may be harmed, if this ring is stiff, but if the pelvis has been kept supple through exercise the transit should be quicker and easier.

AFTER DELIVERY

When the child has been born and the after-birth expelled, the reproductive organs gradually reassume their correct position and size. Other abdominal organs displaced by the enlarged uterus, and muscles that have been greatly stretched in abdomen and pelvic floor, must also be restored to normal. Careful exercising helps and speeds up all these processes. It is also important in preventing the formation of clots or congestion in uterus or veins; in reconditioning muscles stretched, perhaps strained during labour—a common cause of post-natal backache; in discouraging constipation, varicose veins and bad posture; in restoring the figure to its correct proportions and helping the mother regain her vigour, vitality and beauty. Exercise also benefits the supply of milk, which is particularly susceptible to emotional and mental upsets. Nerviness, agitation, anger, anxiety all affect it and react on the child. Good health and calm nerves are essential for successful breast-feeding.

If there is nothing to forbid it, such as stitches, and medical approval is given, the mother could start exercising while still in bed.

First—and this could be practised by all—must come deep breathing, to not only recharge with energy and purify the bloodstream but to gently massage the abdominal organs. By stimulating circulation this also discourages congestion and possible blood clots.

Since the patient is usually propped up in bed after delivery, to drain the uterus, breathing exercises could be done in this position; or, if there is no medical objection, lying flat on the back. If it is awkward to move the arms, concentrate on inhalation-exhalation and the movement of the diaphragm, completely filling and emptying the lungs with each breath.

Recharging by breath with the finger-tips resting on the solar-plexus (Fig. 10) is recommended . . . lying on the back, either with legs straight or crossed and drawn up; also the *Pose of a Fish* (plate 25), modified, with legs crossed and drawn up and arms crossed behind the head with a palm under each shoulderblade. This could also be done with legs stretched.

Before leaving the subject of childbirth it might be relevant to quote the Tantric attitude to maternity. It will be remembered that the Tantrics identify all women with the Supreme Mother, and though the *Mahanirvana Tan-*

tra says that 'The child should regard its mother and father as two visible, incarnate Deities' there is no question which is held to be the greater.

'In glory the mother surpasses the father a thousand times . . . The mother is an object of greater glory than the father because she holds the child in her womb and nourishes it.' . . . 'in the proportion of seed and blood, the quantity of blood, which is the mother's portion, is

FIG. 10

the greater. For this reason the mother's contribution . . . is the greater. At the very outset this gives to the mother superiority over the father. Next comes the pregnancy for ten months and ten days. During this period the Jiva's destiny lies engraved on the foundations of the mother's body. The child's body is built and developed according to her thoughts, her doings, and the humours and blood flowing in her body.'

'After this, again, for five years the child drinks the mother's milk. Taking all these matters together, it appears that the child's indebtedness to the mother permeates his veins, arteries, bones, marrow, vital airs, body, senses, mind and indeed, every molecule and atom from the tip of his toe to the top of his head. His indebtedness to his father is only in respect of the act of procreation. This is the law of nature. The child's indebtedness to his father for acts done subsequent to procreation, such as . . . education, maintenance and so forth, is not such as must naturally appertain to the father, for in his absence these acts may be done by any other guardian. For this reason it does not matter very much to the child if the father dies after procreation; but if the mother dies after conception, not even the united power of the three worlds can supply her place.'

'Under the weight of this great and solemn glory the Shastras ordaining household duties have, with heads bowed down said: "The mother is a thousand times more glorious and more worshipful than the father." '

PRE-NATAL EXERCISES TO STRETCH PELVIC FLOOR AND PELVIC OUTLET, GIVE STRENGTH AND MOBILITY IN WHOLE PELVIC AREA AND FACILITATE LABOUR.

1. With hands on hips and feet slightly apart, practice a half-squatting movement—1—2—3-up.

2. In same position, come up on the toes, then right down into full squatting pose, then up; down; up; down.

3. Keeping feet together, try to sit down as though on an invisible chair . . . soles flat on the floor, back straight.

4. Come down into full squatting position, then, steadying yourself with arms stretched forward, come back till the soles are flat on the floor (Fig. 11).

FIG 11.

5. Lying on the back. Raise left leg to right-angles with floor. Swing it over to the left till the toes touch the floor; then up again and down. Repeat with right leg.

6. Raise both legs to right-angles with the floor and keeping them straight, swing from side to side, like a pendulum, twisting only from the waist.

7. From the same starting position, cross and re-cross the legs, several times.

8. On back with knees bent and feet flat on the floor. Swing both legs over to the right, then the left, to right, to left, twisting only from the waist.

9. In same position but one leg at a time . . . right leg down, up; left leg down, up . . . Let the leg come right down to touch the floor.

10. In same position but moving both legs . . . letting them fall apart and outward, then together—apart, in a very relaxed way—then together.

11. Standing with hands on hips. Raise right leg with knee bent, then move it to the side, forward, side, forward. Down. Repeat with left leg.

12. Reclining on back, propped up with elbows. Draw right knee up to body, then across to right and down in a circular motion, stretching the leg halfway through the circle, then drawing knee up again. Repeat with other leg.

13. In same position, circling both legs together . . . Knees up, across, down (legs stretched) up again, feeling movement in pelvis (Fig 12).

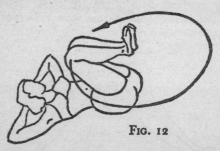

FIG. 12

14. Sit in the Free Pose . . . legs not crossed but so placed that one heel is touching the body between the legs and the other is directly in line with it. The knees are far apart and should, if possible, touch the ground. (A straight line could be drawn down centre of body and heels). Hands rest on knees. Inhale, exhale and bend forward, placing hands palm downward on the floor in front and resting the forehead on the hands.

15. In same position. Inhale and exhale stretching forward with arms extended and kept straight till arms and

forehead rest on the floor. Try to attain this forward-stretching of the arms without rising up at the back (Fig. 13).

FIG. 13 ·

16. Sitting on the floor with legs stretched and together. Move the left leg round, keeping it stiff, by degrees, till it is at right angles with the right leg . . . the movement resembles the hands of a clock. Then bring it slowly back to starting point and repeat. Practise with other leg (Fig. 14).

FIG. 14

17. Stand with hands on hips and feet slightly apart. Practise moving the pelvis back and forth, then from side to side, then in a rotary movement—like a hula.

18. Sit on the floor with knees apart and soles of feet together. Holding the ankles, rock from side to side, taking the weight on the buttocks. This is a form of self-mas-

sage which stimulates circulation in the area of the rectum and discourages haemorrhoids.

TO IMPROVE POSTURE IN PREGNANCY

1. Lie on the floor, trying to make contact between floor and spine, specially in the small of the back, manipulating muscles of abdomen in a pressing-down movement. This is very important when there is a tendency to curvature.

2. On the floor, on back; keeping legs straight, raise them to angle of 45° with the floor (Fig. 15).

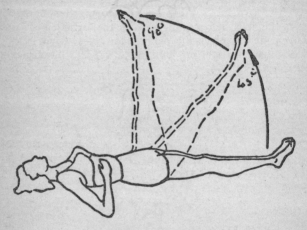

FIG. 15

3. The same movement, but raising them to right angles with the floor (Fig. 15).

4. On the back with hands clasped behind the head (or by the sides); knees bent and drawn up, feet flat on the floor. Keeping knees and feet in same position, try to raise only head and shoulders.

5. Lying on the floor, arms by sides; raise chest only, arching spine.

6. In same position, raise buttocks only, arching spine and keeping heels and shoulders on the floor.

Asanas recommended for pregnancy include the following: Lotus position (page 125); Half-lotus (plate 11, in insert); Pose of an Adept (page 127); Pose of a Fish (plate 25, in insert); Scales Pose (plate 34, in insert). Also Pose of a Hero (plate 12, in insert); Star Pose (plate 31, in insert); Splits (plate 33, in insert). Forward-stretching—so long as comfortable, with following variations; One leg stretched, other in half-lotus; with both legs crossed; Arch gesture (plate 32). Also practise:

Yoga and Childbirth

FIG. 16

Pose of a Frog (plate 13); Pose of a Cat (page 138); Shoulderstand (plate 1) and Half-shoulderstand (plate 2); *Aswini-mudra* (page 128); *Savasana* (page 24) and breathing cycles.

POST-NATAL EXERCISES

Sitting up in bed. For shoulders and spine; to improve posture and stimulate roots of spinal nerves. 1. Bring both shoulders back together in a slow continuous shrugging movement. The arms go back with the shoulders, then forward as the shoulders come down and forward. Movement should be felt in the joints of the spine and between the shoulderblades. After five or six backwards movements reverse and bring the shoulders forward, hunching them while the arms come forward, down and back. (The arms hang limply; they do not move independently of the shoulders.) Repeat five or six times, always with a slow, continuous, unjerky motion.

Now rotate the shoulders alternately—the movement is almost identical with swimming backstroke without full use of the arms. As the left shoulder goes back the right one comes forward. The vertebrae rotate in their sockets, the roots of the spinal nerves are toned up by increased circulation and the tendency to become crouched or round shouldered, so common in bed, is discouraged. These simple but important movements could be practised as often as you like, with your doctor's approval.

Practice tensing every muscle in the body, including stomach, buttocks, thighs, vagina and anus. Inhale as you tense; exhale as you relax.

Sit up with soles of feet together and hands holding the ankles. Rock from side to side, massaging the buttocks. This movement promotes better circulation in the area of anus, perineum and vagina.

For the stomach. With arms over head, inhale and stretch upwards, tensing every muscle, including abdomen; exhale and relax.

With hands behind head (alternatively by the sides). Inhale and raise only the head, feeling stress on stomach muscles; exhale and relax.

On back, arms by sides; inhale and raise only hips; exhale and relax. This could be done with knees bent and feet flat on bed.

On back, inhale and draw the knees up to the stomach; exhale and slowly lower them, feeling stress on stomach.

Practise also the first movement of *Uddiyana*—the contraction of the stomach—as follows:

Sitting up—cross legs if possible—or lying on the back or on the side, inhale, completely exhale and draw the stomach right in as though to touch the spine. Normally this contraction is quite vigorous but as practised here it would be better to do it slowly and gradually, with firmness but without any sudden jerking.

For circulation in feet and legs. Sitting or lying—move toes up and down several times.

Raise and lower feet several times, exercising ankles.

Circle feet, one after the other, at the ankles, round to the right several times, round to the left several times.

Make kicking-out movements from the knees down, as

though shaking something off the feet . . . one leg at a time.

For hips. 'Walking' on the buttocks with hands on hips and sitting with legs stretched . . . forward several 'steps' then backwards.

For chest. Lying on the back, inhale and raise only the chest; exhale and relax.

Out of bed. When you are able to get up and do exercises properly continue to practise all those you did in bed, supplementing or varying them with the following:

For stomach. Half reclining, on back, supported on elbows, draw right knee up to touch shoulder vigorously several times; then repeat with other leg.

Also stomach exercises nos. 6, 7, 9, 11, 12, 13, 14, 16, 17, in Chapter 6.

Standing with legs apart and arms stretched at sides. Bend down and touch right foot with both hands, then come up, spreading arms apart and at the same time leaning back. Repeat twice, then practise on other side (Fig. 16).

With legs apart and hands on backs of thighs. Bend down and press the head to the right knee, come up and press to left knee. The hands should slide down the backs of the legs to grasp the ankles as you bend forward.

Practise full *Uddiyana* and *Nauli;* Cobra; Bow; Supine Pelvic; Pose of a Swallow; Spinal Twist, Solar plexus pose.

For the bust. Each exercise to be done four times.

Practise movement as if pulling down on a rope, tensing the chest muscles, then relaxing and pulling down again.

With closed fists together in front of the chest, pull them apart as though against resistance, till in line with the shoulders; then together; repeat.

With arms stretched forward (parallel) and fists clenched. Pull apart as though against resistance till arms are stretched at sides, leaning back as you pull.

Same movement, but as you open arms turn to the right, twisting from the waistline; come forward and repeat, turning to the left.

With arms stretched at the sides, clench fists and bring

them together in a scooping movement till they meet in front of the chest. Apart again, then scooping again.

In all these exercises the point of concentration must be the muscles of the chest, specially those at the sides near the arms which help to support the breasts.

Also to improve posture and prevent the head becoming poked forward, strengthen the muscles at the back of the neck by the following:

With hands clasped behind the neck, press forward and down, at the same time resisting with the neck muscles. A tension should be felt in this area. The exercise also keeps mobile the prominent bone at the top of the spine which in some women later develops into Dowager's Hump.

Swing the arms up at the sides with elbows bent, bringing shoulderblades together, then tighter together; let arms come down. Repeat several times.

Start with fingertips on shoulders; then push out at the sides against the air in an undulating movement.

With arms stretched at sides and palms down: keeping arms straight, raise up, up, up, in little 'steps' till almost meeting over head; then down and start again.

With arms stretched at sides and kept straight: rotate them in small circles, forward, increasing size of circle; then reverse and circle backward, making smaller circles.

For the pelvic floor and vagina. Practised sitting or lying on the back.

Contract and relax the muscles as in the adaptation of *Aswini-mudra* described on page 128. This is most important in preventing slackness in the vaginal muscles and also improves the circulation in these areas.

Aswini-mudra in its classical form should also be practised to discourage piles or haemorrhoids which often result from childbirth.

Sitting, or lying, contract the muscles of the buttocks, tightening them and pulling them in so you can feel your hips become smaller.

Practice also Pose of a Swallow (page 133); Solar plexus pose (page 136); Cobra (plate 21, in insert); and Bow Pose (plate 23, in insert).

Waistline, pelvis and hips. Practise as many of the movements as you can from Chapter 6.

On the back, raise both legs to vertical, then let the calves fall down—as though the knees have given way. The thighs remain vertical, the calves drop limply. Repeat till slightly tired.

On back, draw knees up to stomach then across and down in a circular movement, pivoting on the hips, and twisting from the waistline. Halfway through the circle the legs are stretched, then knees drawn up again on the other side, brought across the stomach and on down again (Fig. 12).

Practice also pregnancy exercises and all the pelvic *asanas:* Pose of a Cat, also the variation in which the hips are moved from side to side; Supine Pelvic pose; Spinal Twist; all *asanas* with legs in Lotus position; Bridge pose; Angular pose; Star pose; Forward-stretching, including Arch gesture and variations, and Splits; Sideways Swing and Solar plexus pose.

8

Asanas

Asanas to improve health, potency and sexual efficiency.

SHOULDERSTAND (Plate 1)

Shoulderstand is one of the most important *asanas* in
yoga. Its power to restore youth or delay further ageing is
due to the extra supply of arterial blood which is sent to
thyroid and para-thyroid glands, toning them up and thus
benefiting the entire endocrinal system.

Lie down and slowly lift legs and body into a vertical
position, trying to make one straight line from the shoulders. Support the back by placing hands in the region of
the shoulderblades. Chin should be held against the chest
to effect pressure on the thyroid and para-thyroid glands.
Close your eyes, establish deep and rhythmical breathing
and concentrate on the benefits of the pose; on its power
to delay bodily ageing; to restore vigour and vitality.
Hold the position for as long as you comfortably can,
then slowly bring the feet down over the head, into
Plough pose, trying to rest toes on the floor for a few moments, while you concentrate on the roots of the spinal
nerves. To finish, slightly bend the legs and slowly bring
them back to starting point with spine on the floor; then
completely relax.

Purpose: Tones up thyroid gland and sex glands. Restores failing libido and vitality. Helps correct impotence,
premature ejaculation, enlarged prostate, menstrual troubles, haemorrhoids, constipation, prolapsed uterus. Beneficial in puberty, in early pregnancy and in menopause,

particularly with hot flushes. Delays ageing. Used for sub-limative techniques in celibate practice.

HALF-SHOULDERSTAND (Plate 2)

This *asana* differs from the previous one in the position of chin and back. The chin is not pressed to the chest and the hands support the hips instead of the back. An extra supply of arterial blood is thus directed to the face. Facial muscles should be perfectly relaxed and the mind should hold the image of yourself, youthful and unchangeable. Half-shoulderstand nourishes skin and tissues of the face and prevents—in some cases destroys—wrinkles. For the most satisfactory results it should be practised regularly over a considerable period, preferably at the same time of the day. To conclude the pose, bring the legs slowly down over the head, bending the knees and taking hold of the toes, stretch out the legs and retain position, keeping legs as straight as possible. Come down and relax completely for a few moments.

Purpose: Tones up pituitary gland and nervous centres in the head. Beneficial in pregnancy, delaying facial ageing, impotence, prostate enlargement, prolapse, haemorrhoids, constipation. Used for sublimation and transmutation.

TRIANGULAR POSE OR POSE OF TRANQUILLITY (Plate 3)

The name of this *asana* indicates its effect on the nervous system. By supplying extra arterial blood to a certain nervous centre at the back of the head it brings about complete pacification of nerves and mind. Since this leads to better and more restful sleep the position is recommended in cases of insomnia.

Lie down on your back with the arms stretched on the floor above the head. Keeping the knees straight, raise the legs until they form an angle of 45 degrees with your body; then raise the arms and rest the knees on the palms of the hands. The extended arms form the third side of a triangle. Once mastered, the pose could be held for quite a long period; it is extremely comfortable and soothing. To finish the *asana,* bring the legs down over the head, split the knees apart and try to press them to the ground on each side of the head (plate 4), putting pressure on thyroid and para-thyroid glands. Then slowly return to the position of complete rest.

Purpose: Soothes nervous system and overcomes insomnia. Benefits thyroid, sex glands. Limbers up spine. Improves circulation.

BOUND SHOULDERSTAND (Plate 5)

In this variation of the Shoulderstand the locked position of the legs intensifies the effect on the entire system, increasing the flow of blood to the region of thyroid and para-thyroid glands.

Sit on the floor and lock your legs in the Lotus Position. Lie back and slowly raise the body and legs. You may either support your back with your hands—as in Shoulderstand—or rest the weight of your locked legs on your raised hands. To finish the pose, bring your knees down over the head as close to the floor as you can into the Bound plough pose (plate 6). Conclude with position of complete relaxation.

Purpose: Combines all the benefits of *Sarvangasana* with those of the Lotus position. Restores libido. Overcomes impotence. Used in celibacy for transmutation of energies. Helps correct constipation, haemorrhoids.

The Bound plough pose keeps spine supple; stretches pelvic floor and pelvic outlet; limbers up hips and legs. Used in conjunction with Bound *Sarvangasana* in transmutation exercises.

BALANCING SHOULDERSTAND (Plate 7)

Lie flat on your back on floor, raise the arms over the head. Raise the legs as in other inverted poses but without the support of arms or hands. Try to bring legs and back as close to one straight line as possible, taking weight on top of the shoulders and back of the head.

When balance is established, raise the arms and hold them straight, not touching the legs, (as illustrated), deeply inhaling and exhaling. To complete pose, come down into Choking position, as in Pose of Tranquillity; then lower arms and legs and relax.

Purpose: Stimulates circulation in area of pineal gland. Strengthens spine and back muscles. Delays ageing and helps regulate whole endocrinal system. Beneficial in prolapse, prostate enlargement, menstrual troubles, impotence.

HEAD POSE (*Skull gesture*) (Plate 8)

Head pose is often described as the king of all yoga *asanas,* because of its profound and far-reaching effects on the whole system. The body is turned against central gravity forces and the flow of arterial blood to the head is greatly increased, nourishing vital nervous centres and glands in the brain. Gravitational pull is counteracted, displaced vital organs are helped to return to correct position. Deep and rhythmical breathing must be maintained to oxygenate the arterial blood sent to the brain. Students with high blood pressure, or who are grossly overweight or in poor health should not practise this *asana.*

Kneel down on a rug or carpet, making sure it will not slip about. Interlace your fingers and place your hands on the floor, resting on the outer edges of the palms so that a little fence is formed. Lean forward and put your head into this little enclosure, placing the back of head against hands (do not put head *on* hands). Straighten your legs and begin to walk in towards your body. When you cannot get any closer, try to bring your legs up, with knees bent. It may be necessary to kick the legs up at first, until abdominal muscles are strong enough to raise them gradually. Slowly straighten the legs out until the whole body is in a straight line. The elbows and forearms should be kept almost parallel and fairly close together, since they are holding part of the weight, and help in balancing. Do not arch the back—the spine should be as straight as possible. To come down, slowly bring the knees down and in towards the stomach, in a folding-up movement; then gradually lower the legs until the feet are on the ground. Head position should not be practised without help of a teacher or competent person, in the beginning. It should not be held for more than half a minute at first but after it is mastered the time could be extended to two minutes. Prolonged practise should be done only with the approval of an experienced teacher.

Always relax for a few minutes after practising this pose.

Purpose: Tones up pituitary and all other endocrinal glands. Restores fading libido and virility. Increases energy and delays ageing. Discourages impotence, premature ejaculation, menstrual disorders; improves prolapsed uterus, haemorrhoids, enlarged prostate. Important *asana* in sublimative techniques, also with variations of leg positions.

INVERTED EAGLE (Plate 9)

Come into the Headstand, either with the arms in the classical position, or in the meditative pose. For this, kneel down with arms folded on the chest, then place them—still folded—on the floor. Proceed as in classical Headstand. When balance is assured, wind the right leg round the left (from the front), and hook the right foot behind the left calf. May be repeated on other side.

Purpose: Though a sublimative pose for celibate practice, combining pressure on male sex organs with reversal of gravity pull (seat of sex energy placed above seat of physical or mental energy) this pose also gives all the benefits of the classical Headstand.

INVERTED PAGODA. INVERTED TREE

Holding the Headstand, place soles of the feet together and slowly lower them towards the body, bending knees apart, till feet can be brought no further down. Alternatively, practise *Inverted Tree pose* (Plate 10). Kneel down, stretch out the arms at the sides and place backs of the hands on the floor. Place head on the floor and slowly raise the legs into the Headstand, taking weight on head and backs of hands. When upright, split legs apart and hold pose, inhaling and exhaling.

Purpose: All usual benefits of Headstand, but also used as a sublimative pose, for both male and female.

INVERTED PADMASANA

Come up into the classical Headstand, then carefully bend the right knee and work the foot down against the left leg until it is in the region of the groin. Then try to repeat the process with the left leg until both legs are locked in the Lotus position. This pose demands complete steadiness in Headstand and extreme limberness in hip joints and ability to perform *padmasana* with ease. Even so, it is usually necessary for a second person to help put the legs in position in the early stages.

Alternatively, lock the legs in the Lotus position and then try to come up into the Headstand.

Purpose: The benefits combine all those of the Headstand with those of *padmasana*. The pose is used in celibacy practice because of the reversed position and the pressure of the heels against the body.

Purpose of all sitting positions: All cross-legged positions have similar effects, in varying degrees . . . stretching pelvic floor and outlet and limbering up legs and hip joints (and thus important in pregnancy and in increasing sexual efficiency). In Lotus and Half-lotus poses the position of the heels (pressed against the body) is an aid in techniques for overcoming sexual desire. (See Chapter 2, celibacy practices).

LOTUS POSITION or Buddha Pose (*Padmasana*)

This is one of the most important cross-legged positions in yoga. The interlocking of both legs, the heels effecting pressure on the main arteries near the groins, gradually slow down circulation in the legs and increase the supply of blood to the upper part of the body, stimulating and clarifying the process of thought. *Padmasana* may present some difficulty to western students, though it is sometimes mastered in a few months. At first it should be practised for only a few minutes—gradually increasing the time. It is used for many meditative techniques, breathing exercises and *pranayamas*.

BOUND PADMASANA

Sit in the Lotus-position, bringing the feet as far up into the groin as possible. Reach round behind the back with the *right* arm and take hold of the *right* foot (which is in the *left* groin); then do the same with the left arm and foot. The body is now completely bound and pressure of the heels is intensified. After holding this pose for any length of time and overcoming its discomfort, a disembodied feeling is experienced. Celibate yogis practise it while concentrating upon complete suppression of sexual urge. Traditionally, it is concluded by bending forward till forehead touches the ground, putting extra pressure on the lower part of the abdomen. The mind is held upon expulsion of all sex urge from the body.

Purpose: Apart from its use in suppression, Bound *padmasana* develops extreme limberness of back, arms and hip joints. Though inadvisable during pregnancy, it could be valuable preparation for this condition, if the student is sufficiently supple, since it stretches pelvic floor and outlet, strengthens the whole pelvic area and increases circulation in ovaries and reproductive organs.

HALF LOTUS (Plate 11)

Half-lotus differs from full Lotus in that only one foot is placed close to the groin, while the other heel remains on the floor, pressed to the *yoni* place. This is one of the traditional meditative poses of yoga and is very often practised as an alternative to *padmasana* or Pose of an Adept.

POSE OF AN ADEPT

Bring the left foot close to the body and place the right foot between the left calf and the thigh. This pose is greatly valued by eastern teachers as being comfortable and beautifully balanced. It is used for many mental techniques of higher training.

POSE OF A HERO (Plate 12)

An important sitting pose for celibate yogis, and also associated with mental exercises for developing inner strength. (It is said to have been taught to Alexander the Great, during his invasion of India.)

Sit with back and neck in one straight line. Bend the right leg back at the side and place the left foot up on the right thigh in the Half-lotus position. Hold the pose, deeply breathing in and out, with the mind concentrated on the thought of developing inner strength and courage. Change the position of the legs, continuing the concentration. When used for suppression or transmutation, the breathing and concentration are as in the cross-legged poses described in Chapter 2.

Purpose: Stretches pelvic floor and outlet and limbers up legs and hip joints. Is thus important in pregnancy and in increasing sexual efficiency.

POSE OF A FROG (Plate 13)

Kneel down, move knees wide apart, keeping the toes together, and sit back on the feet. Raise the arms over the head with palms together and hold the pose, inhaling and exhaling, concentrating on full abdominal breathing.

Purpose: To improve breathing; soothes nerves; massages abdominal organs through diaphragm movement; stretches pelvic floor and outlet. Beneficial in pregnancy; also used in celibate practise.

YOGA-MUDRA (Plate 14)

Lock the legs in the Lotus position. With arms behind the back, hold the right wrist with the left hand (or vice versa). Inhale, exhale and bend forward till the forehead touches the floor, at the same time raising the arms behind as shown in the illustration.

Purpose: Used as sublimative exercise for celibate yogis. Stretches pelvic floor and outlet. Limbers up hips and leg joints. Tones up abdominal and reproductive organs. Stimulates brain and facial tissues by bringing blood to the head.

ASWINI-MUDRA

Sit with legs crossed, or sit back on the heels. Inhale, exhale and with exhalation contract the muscles of the anus, trying to draw up and inward. Hold; then relax. Inhale; exhale while contracting, then relax. Repeat the cycle as often as comfortable until you are able to perform it quickly and smoothly. The contraction accompanies *exhalation.* The same movement may be adapted for the vagina in women. (See page 89)

Purpose: Primarily for use by celibate yogis, may also be practised with benefit in pregnancy and after childbirth; to improve sexual efficiency (toning up vaginal muscles); to correct haemorrhoids, prostate enlargement, prolapsed uterus and menstrual irregularities.

DANGEROUS POSE (Plate 15)

Sit with the *left* knee bent so that the *left* foot rests at the *right* side of the body; then cross the *right* leg over it so the *right* foot is at the *left* side of the body. Knees are one above the other and hands rested upon the uppermost knee, palms down. Eyes are focussed on the tip of the nose. Hold the pose, inhaling and exhaling.

Purpose: Used mainly for sublimative exercises by celibate yogis. Limbers knee joints. Could discourage haem-orrhoids and prostate enlargement.

POSE OF A TREE (Plate 16)

This is one of the balancing *asanas* which not only de-velop physical equilibrium but contribute to inner peace and tranquillity. It is often recommended for students suffering from nervous disturbances.

Stand on the left foot, lift the right foot and place it close to the left groin, with the sole of the foot turned up. Raise your arms over your head, putting palms together. Focus your eyes on the tip of your nose, or on an empty space about six inches in front. Hold, as long as you com-fortably can, rhythmically breathing in and out, with mind concentrated on inner peace. Change the leg and practise for the same amount of time on the other side.

Purpose: Increases power of balance and mental tran-quillity. Stimulates ovaries by position of foot against body. Limbers up hip and leg joints. Used in sublimation and transmutation exercises.

EAGLE POSE (Plate 17)

This balancing pose is also practised for the purpose of sublimation. It involves a certain amount of pressure on the lower part of the stomach and genital organs.

Stand upright, slightly bend the left leg and wind the right leg around it as shown in the illustration. Bend for-ward a little and wind the arms into similar position to the legs. The elbow of the underneath arm rests on the right thigh, and the chin is pressed on the back of the hand. The eyes are focussed on the tip of the nose. Hold this pose, deeply and rythmically breathing in and out, while concentrating on whatever purpose has been sug-gested by *guru*.

As in all balancing poses, it should be practised on both sides.

Purpose: As a balancing pose, brings tranquillity and

equilibrium. Tones-up sex glands and helps correct sterility. Used in sublimation and transmutation.

KNEE-FOOT POSE (Plate 18)

This advanced *asana* requires suppleness of knees, insteps and hip joints. Sit on the floor with the legs outstretched. Bend the right leg and place the heel as close to the groin as possible, as though to perform Half-lotus position. Slowly bend the left leg and put the foot flat on the floor close to the body. Rise into upright position and place the right knee in line with the left foot. The hands are held in position of prayer. Breathe deeply and rhythmically and, as in Eagle position, concentrate as suggested by the teacher. This could be either on inner tranquillity, or upon suppression of sexual desire, or on sublimation of physical or mental powers. Foot-to-knee pose is a favourite with celibate yogis, who may hold it for long periods. It should be practised on both sides.

Purpose: Loosens up hip and leg joints. Improves balance and mental equilibrium. Pressure of heel against groin tones up ovaries in women and in men is used as part of sublimative techniques.

ANGULAR POSE (Plate 19)

Angular pose combines the properties of the balancing positions and the stretching *asanas*. Every part of the body is stretched and the performance requires considerable control.

Sit on the floor with the feet together and knees apart. Hold the big toes, slowly stretch legs out and up, at the same time leaning back slightly. Jerking will upset the balance. Hold for a few seconds, then come down. It is usually repeated several times.

Purpose: Tones up solar-plexus, pacifies nerves and improves balance. Important in pre-natal training. Improves circulation in rectum and sex organs and is therefore beneficial in prostate enlargement and haemorrhoids. Practised by celibate yoginis.

POSE OF A MOUNTAIN (Plate 20)

On a thick pad or mat, lock the legs in the Lotus position, then try to rise up and stand on the knees with the hands over the head, palms together.*

Purpose: Stretches pelvic floor and outlet; limbers up hips and leg joints; develops balance and stability. Used for sublimative exercises.

COBRA (Plate 21)

In many respects, Cobra has a similar effect on the body to the Pose of a Bow.

Lie face downwards, with palms on the floor, level with the chest and feet stretched out flat. Inhale and push up, lifting the head, neck, chest and abdomen upwards and backwards, contracting the muscles in the small of the back so that a powerful pressure is felt in that region. From the navel downwards the body should be pressed to the floor. Retain position for a few seconds, holding the breath, then exhale and come back to starting point. The movement should be slow and continuous, upwards combined with inhalation, downwards with exhalation.

Purpose: Limbers up spine and back muscles; regulates adrenal glands and ovaries; improves circulation in reproductive organs and corrects menstrual irregularities.

THE LOCUST (Plate 22)

To perform the Locust pose, lie face downwards on the floor with arms either close to the sides or under the thighs. Clench the fists, turning them so that the thumbs touch the floor. Then with a quick movement inhale deeply and raise the legs, keeping them close together. Hold breath and position for a few seconds, then lower legs slowly and exhale. This *asana* may be repeated sev-

---

* May also be performed on alternate sides, as illustrated.

eral times. It has a profound effect upon adrenal glands and kidneys.

Purpose: Tones up adrenal glands, keeps spine supple and strengthens back muscles. Firms and slims stomach and increases circulation in reproductive organs and sex glands. Recommended for impotence, premature ejaculation, to improve sexual efficiency and restore failing libido.

BOW POSE (Plate 23)

Lying on the floor face downwards, bend your legs and take hold of your ankles. Inhale and raise the head and shoulders, at the same time pulling on the ankles to form the body into a bow. Hold briefly, then relax. Repeat several times.

Purpose: Apart from firming thighs, buttocks, this position slims the abdomen and develops the bust. Limbers up spine and back muscles; stimulates the spinal nerves and regulates adrenal glands and ovaries. Improves circulation in reproductive organs and corrects menstrual irregularities.

SUPINE PELVIC POSE (Plate 24)

Kneel down, separate the feet and sit back on the floor between the thighs. Arch the spine and come back till the crown of the head rests on the floor. Hands are held in position of prayer, while inhaling-exhaling is practised. As a variation, the feet could be kept together so the buttocks rest on the heels while the spine is arched.

Purpose: Tones up sex organs in male and female; limbers spine and pelvic area; stimulates adrenal glands; firms thighs.

BRIDGE POSE

Lying on the back, raise the hips, with feet flat on floor and knees bent, and place the hands under the small of the back. Fingers are pointing towards the feet and weight of the body is taken on the palms of the hands and elbows. Keep the elbows close to the sides. When position is assured, stretch the legs out and forward, keeping them close together and with the soles of the feet flat on the floor. The knees should now be straight with body and legs forming an arch. The head is bent back until the crown rests on the floor.

Purpose: Often practised after Inverted cycle, to exercise spine in opposite direction. Keeps spine supple, stimulates adrenal glands. Beneficial in cases of menstrual difficulties and impotence, by toning up reproductive organs.

POSE OF A SWALLOW

Lie face downward on the floor with hands under the chin, palms down, and elbows out at sides. Inhale and rise up from the waist, arching spine and at the same time opening out the arms, as though in a Swallow Dive. Keep the feet on the floor. Exhale and come down. Repeat several times.

Purpose: Stimulates adrenal glands, keeps spine supple, strengthens and slims stomach. Improves circulation in reproductive organs.

FISH POSE (Plate 25)

For this *asana* the legs should be locked in the Lotus position, but if this is not possible cross them in the ordinary way. Lean back, lower the body to the floor, arching the spine, and rest on the crown of the head. The arms may be either stretched forward with the hands holding toes, or they may be folded under the back of the neck. In a third position, arms are stretched out on the floor above the head. While practising this pose concentrate on deep and rhythmical breathing, bearing in mind that the top part of the lungs are getting the fullest benefit, being completely free and empty. Fish pose is recommended after the Plough position, (the second part of Shoulder-

stand; Page 120). It bends the spine in the opposite way
and thus counteracts any strain or stiffness that may be
experienced after this *asana*. It also puts pressure on
adrenal glands.

Purpose: Tones up adrenal and sex glands; regulates
menstruation and keeps reproductive organs healthy. Corrects constipation, haemorrhoids, prolapse of uterus.
Stretches pelvic floor and outlet. Improves impotence and
premature ejaculation.

SPINAL TWIST (Plate 26)

This is an important *asana* in maintaining a healthy spine
and supplying arterial blood to spinal nerves. It is also
one of the most powerful mediums for delaying physical
ageing.

Bring the right heel close to the body and step with
your left foot over right knee. Lock the left knee under
your right armpit, placing left arm behind the back.

Inhale. Slowly exhale, twisting right round to the left,
with your mind's eye concentrated on your spine. Each
moveable vertebra should rotate in its socket, while the
roots of the spinal nerves are toned-up and invigorated. A
stimulating sensation of increased vitality and well-being
may be felt immediately.

Always repeat the position on the other side of the
body.

Purpose: Limbers up spine and invigorates roots of spinal nerves. Slims stomach, increases mobility of joints.
Regulates adrenal glands and sex glands. Recommended
in cases of impotence, premature ejaculation, sterility.

UDDIYANA or stomach contraction (Plate 27)

This extremely important yoga exercise has a powerful
effect on the digestive system. It increases eliminative
power and leads to internal cleanliness. It may be practised either in a sitting or standing position, *always* on an
empty stomach and *only* by those in normal health. It is

not recommended for women during menstruation or pregnancy.

To obtain the full benefit, *Uddiyana* should be made part of the morning routine, practised before breakfast and before opening the bowels.

Standing: With feet about 12 inches apart and palms resting on the thighs, high up, with fingers turned inward, inhale a full breath, then completely exhale. Press the chin to the chest, lean forward, taking the weight on the hands and at the same time draw the stomach right in, as though to touch the spine. Try to make a deep hollow under the ribs. Hold the contraction, then relax. As you pull the stomach in (in an upward-diagonal movement) be careful not to inhale. The contraction must be done with the lungs empty.

In the second stage, a flapping movement of the abdomen—in and out—is brought about by rapid contraction and relaxation of abdominal muscles. This is repeated a number of times.

The sitting position is usually Pose of an Adept. The technique is exactly the same.

Uddiyana should never be practised after a meal, especially after eating fish.

Purpose: Corrects constipation, menstrual irregularities, digestive troubles. Tones up sex glands and reproductive organs. Discourages haemorrhoids and enlarged prostate. Beneficial in impotence, premature ejaculation, sterility, failing libido.

NAULI (Plate 28)

Nauli, the advanced technique of stomach contractions, has a more powerful effect on the digestive system. Having mastered *Uddiyana* and drawn in the stomach, the abdominal recti muscles are isolated by contraction, to form a hard column up the middle of the abdomen. They are then contracted on the right side and on the left, leading eventually to a continuous rolling movement—left, centre, right, centre, etc.—which appears as a wave-like movement from left to right across the abdomen. This difficult exercise, which involves re-education of the abdominal muscles, should be practised on a completely empty stomach, before the looking-glass. Contraction of the central recti muscles should be accompanied by a downward-thrusting movement at the base of the abdomen. The muscles are rooted at the pubic bone and when contracted at the base isolation automatically follows. *Nauli* often requires long practice and perseverence.

Purpose: Corrects constipation, menstrual irregularities, digestive troubles. Tones-up sex glands and reproductive organs. Discourages haemorrhoids and enlarged prostate. Beneficial in impotence, premature ejaculation, sterility, failing libido.

HIDDEN PADMASANA (Plate 29)

Lock the legs in the Lotus position; lie down on the stomach and place palms together in position of prayer behind the back.

Purpose: Tones up abdominal region; stretches pelvic floor and outlet. Increases suppleness of hips and legs. Used in celibate practise.

SOLAR PLEXUS POSE (Plate 30)

Sit with feet flat on floor and knees drawn up. Rest the palms on the floor at the sides of the body. Inhale. Stretch out the legs—keeping them straight—to an angle of 45 degrees with the floor, slightly leaning back at the same time. Hold a few seconds; exhale and come down.

Purpose: Increases vital energy by toning-up solar plexus. Strengthens abdominal muscles. Beneficial in impotence. Important in post-natal exercise.

POSE OF A STAR (Plate 31)

Sit with the soles of the feet one against the other, and knees wide apart. The hands rest on the ankles. Inhale; exhale, grasping the feet with both hands and bending forward till forehead touches big toes and elbows rest on the floor, outside the legs. Since this pose is demanding on the inner thighs it should not be forced.

Purpose: Develops suppleness in whole pelvic area, stretches pelvic floor and outlet. Limbers up spine and massages abdominal organs. Reduces waist and stomach. Beneficial in pregnancy, impotence, prostate enlargement, haemorrhoids.

ARCH GESTURE (Plate 32)

Sit with left leg stretched and right foot placed against inside of left thigh. Inhale, exhale and come forward, trying to take hold of the left foot, or ankle, and pressing the head to the stretched knee. Repeat; change sides and practise twice more.

When practised as *maha-mudra,* used for sublimative purposes, the heel is pressed against the *yoni* place, and breath and concentration are adapted for the purpose. This *mudra* is said to arrest the flow of semen and to give many powers and attainments.

Purpose: Exercises and limbers up spine, invigorates roots of spinal nerves; tones up abdominal and reproductive organs. Reduces fat on waist and abdomen; improves circulation in face and in abdominal and reproductive organs. Increases virility.

FORWARD STRETCH (Splits) (Plate 33)

Sit with legs as far apart as possible. Inhale; exhale and lean forward, placing fingers on toes and trying to bring the head to the floor, without bending the knees. As in Star pose, practise gradually.

Purpose: Develops suppleness in whole pelvic area, stretches pelvic floor and outlet. Limbers up spine and massages abdominal organs. Reduces waist and stomach. Beneficial in pregnancy, impotence, prostate enlargement, haemorrhoids.

SCALES POSE (Plate 34)

Lock the legs in the Lotus position, lean back resting on the elbows and raise the locked legs to an angle of about 45 degrees with the floor. Hold, inhaling and exhaling, then come down and unlock legs.

Purpose: Tones up solar-plexus and increases vital energy; strengthens abdominal muscles; stretches pelvic floor and outlet; increases suppleness in hips and pelvis.

SIDEWAYS SWING (Plate 35)

Sit with both legs to one side, arms linked over the head.

Inhale, and as you exhale, swing the body three times over the bent legs. Repeat, then change sides and practise as before.

Purpose: Limbers up spine, tones up adrenal glands, firms waist and stomach muscles.

POSE OF A CAT (Figs. 4A. and 4B.)

On all-fours, keeping the elbows straight, manipulate the spine, moving it up into an arch, then down into concave position, then up again. Only the spine moves . . . arms must not bend.

Purpose: Limbers up spine and tones up roots of spinal nerves. Increases flexibility of whole pelvic area and is thus important in pre- and post-natal exercising and in improving sexual efficiency.

POSE OF AN ARCHER (Plate 36)

Sit with right leg stretched forward, then step over it with the left. (The left foot should be alongside the right knee). Hands are at the sides. Inhale; exhale and at the same time pick up the *left* foot with the *right* hand and try to raise it to touch the forehead, between the eye-brows. The *left* arm is stretched forward till the hand rests on the toes of the *right* foot. Study the illustration. The movement is based upon the action of an archer, and the arm that is shooting the arrow (pulling the foot up to the forehead) should be kept out and away from the body, with elbow pointing upward. Hold the pose briefly, then come down and repeat on other side.

Purpose: Keeps spine and joints supple; reduces fat on waist and abdomen; tones up digestive and reproductive organs and increases circulation in these areas. Overcomes constipation and helps correct sexual debility and loss of potency.

RECHARGING BREATHS

A study of controlled breathing could lead to the personal discovery that energy in the human body may literally be replenished not by bread alone but by breath. Yoga has a great many energy-recharging exercises, all based on the principle of tapping individual energy to the energy of the universe through the medium of deep breathing. The flow of *prana* or cosmic energy (see glossary) into the lungs could be increased by improved inhalation. By willpower and concentration this extra energy is then either stored in the solar plexus or directed to any desired part of the system, with invigorating and healing effects. The solar plexus, being the seat of physical energy in the human body, is the point of concentration for many breathing exercises.

RECHARGING IN CROSS-LEGGED POSITION

Sitting in any comfortable cross-legged position, establish deep and rhythmical breathing, forming a mental image of *prana* drawn in with incoming breath, and with out-going, directed to the solar plexus. It is taught that the actual separation of *prana* from the air is brought about by mental concentration.

To increase the effect of this recharging exercise, the

breath is retained after inhalation, with the mind concentrated as above; then after *slow* exhalation an image is formed of static air expelled from the lungs, while the precious life force is stored in the solar plexus. A very efficient recharging method is practised in *Savasana* (page 24), when after complete relaxation and rhythmical breath are established, the fingertips are lightly placed on the region of the solar plexus and the mind concentrated on the life force being directed with each exhalation to this centre (through the fingertips). We are taught that a certain amount of life force continuously escapes into the atmosphere through the fingertips. (This is why a healthy person's palms and fingers possess potential healing power.) Placing the fingertips in the region of the solar plexus, or holding the big toes while deeply and rhythmically breathing closes the circuit of *prana* in the body.

Many recharging exercises are done in the standing position and grouped in traditional cycles. One of these is known as *Vigorous cycle:*

VIGOROUS CYCLE, consisting of seven breaths

(In all these exercises you are exhaling only stale air, retaining *prana* in your solar plexus.)

Inhale full breath and locking it in the chest, swing the arms twice backwards and twice forwards vigorously. Exhale through the mouth.

Stretch the arms forward, and after inhaling a full breath, open them out sideways, swinging at shoulder-height, two or three times. Exhale through the mouth as your arms drop.

Inhale as before, this time swinging the arms up and down, keeping them parallel and slightly arching the small of the back. Exhale and drop the arms.

After the breath is inhaled and locked, slowly stretch the arms forward. Clench the fists and pull them quickly back against the chest, shaking entire body. (Shaking the body while breath is retained features in a number of yoga techniques.)

Inhale; swing arms up over the head and bend the body to the right. Straighten up, arms by sides, then swing them up again and bend to the left. Exhale through the mouth.

Inhale and vigorously massage floating ribs, while breath is retained. Exhale.

Inhale, patting chest while breath is retained. Exhale.

PACIFYING BREATHS

One of the remarkable properties of controlled breath is its pacifying effect on the mind and entire nervous system.

The principle of Pacifying Breath consists of slowing down the normal breathing rhythm between four and six times. (The usual rate is fifteen to twenty breaths per minute; in Pacifying Breathing this is reduced to five or six breaths a minute.) The rhythm is established either by counting heart or pulse beats or by concentrating on the syllable OHM (OM,AUM) using it as a unit of counting: e.g. six heart beats or six OHMs for inhalation, six for exhalation.

A traditional pacifying exercise is to sit in one of the cross-legged positions with the eyes closed and mind *entirely* concentrated on breathing, inhaling and exhaling in this 6–6 rhythm. Success in this exercise depends upon ability to suspend all thought, all mental activity, allowing yourself to become light and free as breath.

NINE PACIFYING BREATHS

The cycle known as Nine Pacifying Breaths pacifies the mind and nervous system quickly and effectively. It is practised standing, with feet together, eyes either closed or concentrated on the tip of the nose. There are three different arm movements: 1. Arms forward, up, and down sideways, describing a circle (four times). 2. Arms up from the sides over the head, with fingertips touching (three times). 3. Arms forward and up, describing parallel lines (twice).

In all these movements inhalation accompanies raising

the arms, exhalation is on lowering them. The rhythm of respiration is extremely slow, not less than six heart beats for incoming and six for outgoing breath. *All breathing, in and out, is done through the nose.*

Table of *Asanas*

CHILDBIRTH, PREPARATION FOR

All cross-legged poses, some poses involving Lotus position. Pose of a Cat. *Aswini-mudra*. Supine pelvic. Frog pose. Exercises in Chapters 6 and 7.

COITAL POSTURES, TRAINING FOR

Exercises in Chapter 6. Cross-legged and Lotus positions. Cat pose. Cobra. Bow. Locust.

CONSTIPATION, TO CORRECT

Uddiyana. Nauli. Headstand. All inverted poses. Fish. Cobra. Bow. Locust. *Yoga-mudra. Aswini-mudra.*

ENERGY, VITAL, TO RESTORE

Breathing cycles. Headstand. *Sarvangasana.* Spinal Twist. *Savasana.* Cobra. Bow. Locust.

GLANDS, ENDOCRINAL

Pituitary:	Headstand
Thyroid:	Shoulderstand
Suprarenals:	Cobra. Bow. Locust. Spinal Twist. Supine Pelvic.

Ovaries: Cobra. Bow. Locust. Eagle Pose. Hidden
                padmasana.

Testes: Fish pose. *Uddiyana. Nauli.* Eagle. Cobra.
(Testicles)   Bow. Locust.

HAEMORRHOIDS

Headstand. All inverted poses. *Savasana. Aswini-mudra.*
massage on page 113–14.

IMPOTENCE

Headstand. All inverted poses. *Savasana. Aswini-mudra.*
Transmuting of sex energy, Chapter 2. Arch gesture.
Yoga-mudra. Maha-mudra.

INSOMNIA

Pose of Tranquillity. *Savasana.* Breathing cycles. Locust.

LIBIDO, TO RESTORE

Headstand. Shoulderstand and all inverted poses. *Savasana.* Breathing cycles.

TO SUPPRESS

See techniques in Chapter 2.

MENOPAUSAL DISORDERS

Savasana. Pacifying and recharging breaths. Cobra.
Spinal Twist. *Uddiyana. Nauli. Aswini-mudra.* Shoulderstand. Pose of Tranquillity.

MENSTRUAL IRREGULARITIES

Cobra. Bow. Locust. *Uddiyana. Nauli.* Supine pelvic. *Aswini-mudra.* Headstand. Shoulderstand. Fish. Hidden *padmasana.*

NERVOUS TENSION

Savasana. Shoulderstand. Pose of Tranquillity Breathing cycles.

PELVIS, TO LIMBER UP

All exercises in Chapters 6 and 7. All Lotus poses. Star pose.

TO STRETCH PELVIC FLOOR AND PELVIC OUTLET

All Lotus poses. Star pose. Forward stretch, with legs apart. Frog pose.

POST-NATAL TRAINING

Exercises in Chapter 7. Headstand. Shoulderstand. *Uddiyana. Nauli.* Cobra. Bow. Locust. Spinal Twist. Archer. *Aswini-mudra.*

PUBERTY DISTURBANCES

Headstand. Shoulderstand. Pose of Tranquillity. *Savasana.* Fish. Hidden *padmasana.* Scales pose. Balancing poses. Cobra. Bow. Locust. Breathing cycles.

PREMATURE EJACULATION

Headstand. Shoulderstand. Pose of Tranquillity. *Savasana*. Spinal Twist. Supine pelvic. Cobra. Bow. *Mahamudra*.

PRE-NATAL TRAINING

Pose of a Cat. All cross-legged, some Lotus poses. *Savasana*. Breathing cycles. Exercises in Chapters 6 and 7.

PROLAPSE OF THE UTERUS

. Headstand. Shoulderstand and all inverted poses. *Aswini-mudra. Uddiyana*.

PROSTATE, ENLARGEMENT OF

Aswini-mudra. Arch gesture. Headstand and all inverted poses. Rocking massage (page 113–14). *Uddiyana*. Some Lotus poses.

SEXUAL EFFICIENCY, TO IMPROVE

Exercises in Chapters 6 and 7. Headstand and all inverted poses. *Savasana*. Cobra. Bow. Locust. Archer. Spinal Twist. All Lotus poses. *Aswini-mudra*. .

SEXUAL DEBILITY

Headstand. Shoulderstand. Solar plexus pose. All inverted poses. Fish pose. Hidden *padmasana*. Scales. Angular pose. Eagle and Inverted Eagle. *Aswini-mudra. Uddiyana. Nauli. Maha-mudra*.

STERILITY

Eagle pose. Headstand and all inverted poses. Cobra. Bow. Spinal Twist. Supine pelvic. *Savasana.*

STOMACH, TO FIRM AND REDUCE

Uddiyana. Nauli. Locust. Archer. Arch gesture. Solar plexus pose. Angular Pose. Exercises in Chapter 7.

SUBLIMATIVE TECHNIQUES

Chapter 2.

SUPPRESSIVE TECHNIQUES

Chapter 2.

TRANSMUTATION OF SEXUAL ENERGY

Chapter 2.

VAGINAL MUSCLES, TO TONE UP AND CONTROL

Aswini-mudra.

WEIGHT, TO REDUCE

Headstand. Shoulderstand. All general practice. All-over body development, strengthening and limbering up, including spine, muscles.

Glossary

AGAMAS	Scriptures (Tantric)
AJNA CAKRA	Nervous plexus between eyebrows. Centre of command
AKARSHANA DHANURASANA	Pose of an Archer
ANAHATA CAKRA	Nervous plexus in the chest
ANANGA RANGA	Ancient book on sex and art of love
APANA	Vital air controlling excretory functions
ARDHA-PADMASANA	Half Lotus
ARDHA-MATSYENDRASANA	Spinal Twist
ASANA	Bodily pose. Third 'limb' (*anga*) of Hatha yoga
ASHRAM	Hermitage
ASWINI-MUDRA	Contraction of anus muscles
ATMAN	Individual spirit; part of Universal Spirit or Brahman
AUM (OM)	All . . . Everything . . . Omnipotence. Used as unit of counting in breath control
AVATARA	One who has reached the supreme stage of development, with full power over life and death and freedom from the law of reincarnation
BHAGAVAD GITA	The Song of God
BHAKTI YOGA	The yoga of love and devotion
BHOGA	Enjoyment
BHUJANGASANA	Cobra pose
BINDU	Sperm; seed
BRAHMAHCAKRA (SAHASRARA)	1,000-petalled lotus; nervous plexus in top of the head

148

BRAMACHARYA	Celibacy
BRAMACHARI	A celibate
BRAHMAN	The Universal Spirit. Divine Principle
CAKRA (CHAKRA)	Nervous plexus of subtle-physical body
CHELA	Disciple—pupil of *guru*
DHANURASANA	Bow pose
DVAPARA	One of the Ages of Man, in Tantrism
GARUDASANA	Eagle pose
GURU	Spiritual guide. One who dispels darkness
HA	The sun—in the word *Ha*tha
HATHA YOGA	Yoga of bodily strength and control
HEVAJRA TANTRA	A Buddhist Tantra
IDA	A *nadi,* or channel of energy starting in left nostril (in subtle-physical body)
ISVARA	God
JAINA YOGI	A member of ascetic Jaina community
JANUSIRASANA	Arch gesture
JINA	'One who has conquered the worldly passions'
JIVA	Living being
JIVANA-MUKTI	'Liberated in life'
KALI YUGA	Dark Age (Tantrism)
KALKI AVATARA	The Rider on the White Horse (Tantrism)
KAMA	God of Lust
KAMA SUTRA	Ancient Indian work on Art of Love, by Vatsyayana
KARMA	Action. Also used for Destiny
KARMA YOGI	One who seeks liberation through right action
KARMIC LAW	The law of cause and effect, involving reincarnation

KARNAPEETASANA	Choking pose
KRISHNA	An incarnation of Vishnu
KUNDALINI	The Coiled Serpent. Latent nervous energy in the body
LINGA	Male sex organ. Emblem of Siva
LOTUS	Symbol of purity. Female sex organ
MAHA-RASA	Sperm. Semen
MANDALA	Complex visual symbol, studied before practice of meditation
MANIPURA CAKRA	Solar plexus
MANTRUM	Sacred sound vibration, audible or silent
MATSYASANA	Fish pose
MUDRA	To lock up or seal. A gesture or posture. In Tantrism may mean a young girl or a grain food
MULADHARA CAKRA	The Root Centre. Nervous plexus at the base of the spine
NADI	Channel of energy in subtle-physical body
NATH YOGIS	Followers of Goraknath
NAULI	Separation of abdominal recti muscles
NIVRTTI	(The way of) Renunciation, in Tantrism
NIYAMA	Observance
OM	see Aum
OORDHVA-PADMASANA	Bound Headstand
PADMA	Lotus. Symbol of purity. Also Female sex organ
PADMASANA	Lotus position
PANCHATATTVA	Ritual of five Elements (Tantric)
PINGALA	*Nadi,* starting in right nostril
PATANJALI	Sage who collected and expounded *yoga sutras*
PRAJNA	Wisdom
PRAKRITI	Nature

PRANA	Cosmic energy; life force; vitality in the air. Inhaled with breathing. Also may be taken into the body from earth and water
PRANA-VAYU	Vital air
PRAVRTTI	(The way of) Desire (in Tantrism)
PRANAYAMA	Study of practice of breath control-'Voluntary interruption of breathing in and out'
PURAKA	Inhalation
PURUSHA	Pure consciousness
RADHA	Maiden loved by Krishna
RAJAH YOGA	The path of complete mental discipline and supremacy
RAJAS	Female seed; Menstrual flow
RASA	Pleasure. In Tantrism . . . practice or observance
RECHARKA	Exhalation
SADDHU	Holy man
SADHAKA	Seeker. Disciple
SADHANA	Spiritual training
SAHAJAYISTS	Members of cult developing from Tantrism . . . Buddhist Sahajayists and Vaisnava Sahajayists . . . seeking Supreme Bliss
SAHASRARA (BRAHMAHCAKRA)	1,000-petalled Lotus; nervous plexus in top of head
SAKTI	Consort of Siva. The Divine Mother. Female principle
SALABHASANA	Locust pose
SAMAHDI	Superconscious state in which Identification (yoga) is realized
SAMHITA	Collection (of texts)
SATTVA	Good, pure
SATYA YUGA	Golden Age, in Tantrism
SARVANGASANA	Shoulderstand. Candle Pose
SAVASANA	Pose of Complete Rest. Pose of a Dead Man
SHASTRA	Scriptures

SIDDHA	One who has developed suprahuman powers
SIDDHASANA	Pose of an Adept
SIDDHI	Attainments. Suprahuman powers
SIRSHASANA	Head Stand
SIVA	God of Indian pantheon
SUKHA	Joy, Delight. Happiness
SUKHASANA	Easy Pose (simple crosslegged)
SUKRA	Male seed
SUPTA-VAJVASANA	Supine Pelvic; Supine Thunderbolt
SUSHUMNA	Central artery
SUTRA	Scriptures
SVA	Self
SVADHISHTHANA CAKRA	'Support of Life Breath' at root of Penis
SWAMI	One seeking the Self. Member of monkish order
TANTRA	Ritual; practice
TANRATATTVA	Principles of Tantra
TANTRIC YOGI	One who seeks liberation according to Tantric teaching
THA	The moon (in Ha-*tha* yoga)
TRETA YUGA	One of the Four Ages of Man, in Tantrism
UDDIYANA	Stomach contractions
UPANISHAD	Sacred Hindu writings
VAJRA	Thunderbolt. Name of *asana*. Also male organ
VAYU	Vital air
VIPAREETA-KARANI	Half-shoulderstand
VISHNU	Hindu god
VAISNAVIST	Follower of Vishnu
VIRASANA	Pose of an Hero
VKRASANA	Tree pose
VISHUDDHA CAKRA	Plexus in throat region
YAMA	Restraint (Yama is also God of Death)

YANTRA	Magical diagram used to aid concentration
YOGA	Union
YOGI	One who seeks liberation through yoga
YOGINI	A female yogi
YONI	Female sex organ
YUGA	Age. The four ages of man, in Tantrism are:
	Satya yuga The Golden Age
	Treta yuga
	Dvapara yuga
	Kali yuga The Dark Age
YUJ	To yoke. (Root of *yoga*)
YUKTA	One who has attained liberation

Index

155

BANTAM BESTSELLERS

OUTSTANDING BOOKS NOW AVAILABLE
AT A FRACTION
OF THEIR ORIGINAL COST!

☐ PSYCHIC PEOPLE by Eleanor Smith. Incredible but true explorations into the strange world of supernatural human powers. (N4471—95¢)

☐ THE RICH AND THE SUPER-RICH by Ferdinand Lundberg. The spectacular $12.50 bestseller about who really owns America, now only $1.95!
(Y4488)

☐ I MARRIED A PRIEST by Joan Longo. The astonishingly honest sequel to her husband's bestseller SPOILED PRIEST. (N4706—95¢)

☐ A MASS FOR THE DEAD by William Gibson. The beautifully written story of how the author grew from boy into man. (Q4568—$1.25)

☐ THOSE INCREDIBLE CHRISTIANS. In this brilliant companion to THE PASS-OVER PLOT, Dr. Hugh Schonfield once again challenges Christian belief.
(Q4372—$1.25)

☐ MEMOIRS 1925-1950 by George Kennan. Two turbulent decades are brought vividly to life in this prize-winning bestseller. (D3872—$1.65)

☐ BLACK RAGE by William H. Grier, M.D. & Price M. Cobbs, M.D. Two black psychiatrists present an overwhelming picture of the desperation of the black man's life in America today. (N3931—95¢)

☐ COFFEE, TEA OR ME? by Trudy Baker and Rachel Jones. A wild and witty look at the jet-age set by two high-flying stewardesses. (N3870—95¢)

☐ REPORT OF THE NATIONAL ADVISORY COMMISSION ON CIVIL DISORDERS. What happened? Why did it happen? What can be done? (QZ4273—$1.25)

☐ A SEARCH FOR THE TRUTH. Ruth (A GIFT OF PROPHECY) Montgomery's startling personal experiences in the psychic world. (N3725—95¢)

☐ A GIFT OF PROPHECY. The startling story of the phenomenal Jeane Dixon, the woman who predicted Kennedy's assassination. (N4223—95¢)

Ask for them at your local bookseller or use this handy coupon:

BANTAM BOOKS, INC., Dept. GA1NF, Room 300,
271 Madison Ave., N. Y., N. Y. 10016

Please mail me the Bantam Bestsellers checked above I am enclosing $_____. (Check or money order—no currency, no C.O.D.'s please. If less than 5 books, add 10¢ per book for postage and handling.) Please allow up to four weeks for delivery.

Name_____

Address_____

City_____State_____Zip_____

GAINF—6/69

BANTAM BESTSELLERS

OUTSTANDING BOOKS NOW AVAILABLE
AT A FRACTION
OF THEIR ORIGINAL COST!

If you think this book was good, wait 'til you see what *else* we've got in store for you!

Send for your FREE catalog of Bantam Bestsellers today!

This money-saving catalog lists hundreds of bestsellers originally priced from $3.75 to $15.00— yours now in Bantam paperback editions for just 50¢ to $1.95! Here is a great opportunity to read the good books you've missed and add to your private library at huge savings! The catalog is FREE! So don't delay—send for yours today!